Lady in Room Number Nine

My Grandmother's Murder at the Empire Hotel

Larry Ohman

LADY IN ROOM NUMBER NINE

MY GRANDMOTHER'S MURDER AT THE EMPIRE HOTEL

This story is based on actual events. In certain cases incidents, characters and timelines have been changed for dramatic purposes. Certain characters may be composites, or entirely fictitious.

ISBN 978-0-578-79199-9

Cover created by Larry Ohman

Manufactured in the United States of America
First printing November 2020

Introduction

On April 18, 1940, Marie Theresa Evans, my maternal grandmother, was brutally beaten at the Empire Hotel in Butte, Montana. Theresa, as her family called her, died at 2:30 a.m. on April 21 at the age of 37. She never regained sufficient consciousness to be able to identify the perpetrator. At the time of the incident, she was a boarder at the Empire Hotel after her fourth husband, Nick Evans, disappeared months earlier. A coroner's inquest was conducted four days after her death. There was a primary suspect who was held in custody until the inquiry concluded. Twelve witnesses testified at the investigation, including six witnesses at the Empire Hotel at the time of the beating and the police detective involved in the case. Two physicians and a mortician testified as to the extent of the injuries, including the subdural hematoma on the cerebral hemisphere, which ultimately caused her death. No one was prosecuted or convicted for the beating and eventual death of my grandmother. The prosecutor elected not to pursue prosecution, for unclear reasons, and the primary suspect was released. Theresa was laid to rest at Mt. Caramel cemetery in Anaconda, Montana, with a simple grave marker. Years later, it was replaced with a granite headstone simply engraved with "Theresa" 1902-1940.

Theresa had a complicated and complex life. She married four times and had five children. Jeanne, my mother, was one of three children from her first marriage to Charles Forster in 1919. She had an older sister by five years, Marie Gertrude, and an older brother by three years, Lawrence Charles, who died of spinal meningitis a month before my mother's birth. Theresa had a son, Raymond, with her second husband, Raymond P. Brown, who died after three years of marriage. They married in 1927. She married her third husband, William Robbins, in 1930, and they had two daughters, Geraldine and Patricia. Robbins later married his stepdaughter, my mother's older sister Marie Gertrude. Theresa married Nick Evans in 1938, her fourth husband. They had no children together.

My mother was thirteen years old when her mother died. She was living with her maternal grandmother Mary Green in nearby Anaconda at the time of her mother's death. She later married my dad, John Ohman, and they had ten children together. They raised eleven children in total as dad adopted my oldest sister, who was from mom's first marriage. Mom was a very private person and rarely talked about her life growing up. It was not until I was in high school that I found out that my grandmother Theresa had been murdered. Mom did not offer details and was reluctant to answer questions though occasionally she would share snippets about her childhood. Mom eventually shared some newspaper articles she had saved regarding the beating and subsequent death.

Over the years, I have often wondered about the details of my grandmother's death and the circumstances surrounding the event. Now, at age 61, I sought to research and chronicle her story. I regret that I did not attempt to do so much earlier. Family members who had real-time knowledge of the event have long since passed on. I have had many discussions with my siblings, and we all have recollections of the few things mom had said about the beating and resultant death. We all recall comments mom mentioned, but a detailed description of the events is not known. It is remarkable to me how little we knew about the event. As a result, I was determined to research and then produce this book to document all that I could find regarding my grandmother's death.

I chose to write this book as a murder mystery. I committed to research and then utilized the facts as I found them. In my study, I found many events that previously were not known by my family, particularly my siblings. But many things are still not known and will likely never be known. Therefore, I elected to write this book in the form of historical fiction, filling in when there are gaps in knowledge. No one was ever convicted of the beating/murder, but there were undoubtedly suspects. I developed characters based on known suspects and a few plausible ones based on comments made by my mother or other family members.

I dedicate this book, first, to the grandmother I never knew. It has been challenging at times, researching the event of her beating and subsequent death. Descriptions of her badly beaten body are difficult to read. Although I never met her, she is part of my family history, a history I now appreciate on a much deeper level.

Secondly, I dedicate this to my mother, who was significantly impacted by this tragic event in her young life. She most certainly had a difficult and challenging young childhood. It undoubtedly shaped her adult life, for which I was privileged to share in part. She was a private person, likely a direct result of her experiences growing up with four different "fathers" and losing her mother at the young age of thirteen. This difficult time of her life undoubtedly shaped her world view.

And thirdly, to my siblings and their children. I hope this book provides them with a deeper understanding of Marie Theresa and our shared family history.

Chapter 1

The gray smoke filled the night sky. As Theresa stepped outside, the pungent smell created by the miners' long workday filled her nostrils. For someone new to the city, the smell was strong and difficult to tolerate, but after several years in town, the Sulphur smell was hardly noticeable anymore to Theresa. As she gazed east, the smoke hung over the skyline, nearly blocking the view of the mighty Rocky Mountains. "The Richest Hill on Earth" at the base of the Continental Divide was slowly eroding and becoming disfigured. A maze of underground shafts infiltrated the entire hillside, and gallows frames dotted the hillside designating the vertical shafts of the dozens of mines. Theresa could easily recognize that the economy of Butte was healthy as mining jobs were available to anyone who was willing to work underground. A variety of businesses had sprung up all around as a result of the mining growth. Unfortunately, there was a high cost for some miners. Theresa heard just this week; two men died while working underground when an ore car crushed them against the shaft wall. Injury and death were common, but the miners accepted the risk for the benefit of stable, good paying jobs.

As Theresa gazed into the distance, she contemplated

the challenging choices she must make. Her life had changed significantly over the past several months. She moved into the Empire Hotel after she lost her apartment when her husband disappeared. The once beautiful Empire Hotel, built in 1892, was now nothing more than cheap boarding rooms for those who had few living options. It was not a particularly desirable place for Theresa, especially since it was located adjacent to the red-light district. It's close proximity to the Dumas Brothel and Pleasant Alley led to its decline as a hotel and its gradual deterioration. Theresa certainly preferred to live somewhere else – almost anywhere else – but her current financial situation did not allow for anything different.

Standing at the hotel's Wyoming Street entrance, the other was on Galena Street, her thoughts drifted to what could have been. It was just a few months ago that she and her husband Nick operated the Belmont Bar. The Belmont was a block east from the Empire, and they were optimistic that they were going to make it a success and eventually become owners. But it was not to be. She never dreamed that her life would take the drastic turns that it has. Not in her worst nightmares would she have predicted she would be in this situation today.

Theresa turned and reentered the Empire. Looking around she could see the remnants of the once fine hotel. Originally named the Copper Block Building, she could almost visualize the beautiful furnishings and the elegant events that once took place there. The now small bar only hinted at the fine bar and restaurant that once occupied the lobby area. She observed the bland décor and deterioration from the neglect over the years. The splintered wooden reception desk obviously hadn't been polished in years and the carpet was stained and heavily worn. Glancing over to the west wall, she saw the elevator that hadn't been operational for years. Against the north wall was the staircase that led to her room on the second floor. The carpeted stairs were threadbare, and the handrail was unstable. As Theresa applied light pressure to the rail, it creaked as if it was going to break. In the opposite corner sat a fireplace burning with the soft, dim glow of its embers. After entering her small room on the second floor, she opened her window to the alley behind the Empire. Pleasant Alley was quiet tonight. The Dumas Brothel sat on the south side of the alley and multiple cribs lined the north side. It wouldn't be long before the activity picked up and the "ladies" began their work night. Theresa couldn't believe her life had come to this – living adjacent to the red-light district with no clear prospects for a way out.

As Theresa readied herself for the evening, she thought about how she had agreed to go to the Belmont Bar tonight. Months had passed since she had last been there. When she and her husband Nick lost the bar, she was convinced she would never return. But when she was invited by a charming man to go drinking and dancing, she couldn't turn him down. She needed a night out to forget about her troubles and to enjoy life again, if just for an evening. She knew it would be a temporary but right now she needed the distraction. Agreeing to meet him there, Theresa walked into the familiar bar situated on the northwest corner of Mercury and Arizona streets. Stepping inside, the L shaped mahogany bar with its fifteen stools looked the same as when she saw them last. The south facing window was dirty and likely hadn't been washed since she left. The small dance floor was empty, but the live music wasn't scheduled to start for another half an hour. In the back of the bar sat two card tables where a few of the local miners were playing poker. They likely had walked from Meaderville, Finntown, or Dublin Gulch – ethnic neighborhoods that surrounded the area. Theresa glanced around, feeling as though everyone there judged her for losing the bar. Palms sweating, she looked around for her "date" and saw him sitting at the bar.

After enjoying a few drinks at the bar, the music began to play. Theresa's new friend asked her to dance and as they did so, she couldn't help but think about the past few months. Her husband Nick had disappeared without a trace and no one had seen him since. Theresa now concluded that it was time to move on, recognizing that he was not likely ever coming back. As she stared into the eyes of this new man, she hoped that this was the beginning of a new relationship that would lead her out of her current circumstances. She also thought about her two children, Jeanne and Raymond, who she left with her mother in Anaconda until her life would become more stable. It had been weeks since she had seen them, and Theresa thought by now the bar would be a success and the children would be there with her. But things had not turned out like she had hoped. Theresa couldn't bring herself to talk with her mother about it, unable or unwilling to admit to another failure. She kept hoping that things would change, would improve, but it was clear that for now her life was failing.

Tonight, had been a very enjoyable evening, romantic even, and Theresa was not ready for it to end. She found herself excited to have this man come back to her room. She wasn't sure what she wanted to happen, but she knew it had been several months since she had any male companionship. She hadn't had great success with her previous relationships, as evidenced by her four previous husbands, but she sensed things were going to be different now. She couldn't seem to help herself; she needed a man in her life, or so she reasoned.

Theresa and the new man walked arm and arm from the Belmont to the Empire. As they arrived at her room, he excused himself to use the restroom down the hall. Theresa sat on her bed, contemplating the recent months of her life. Things had not gone according to her plans, leaving her feeling lost and hopeless in many ways. She was trying to be optimistic about her future, but she found it very hard to be so. Theresa determined that tonight was going to be the start of the new Theresa Evans. Her life was about to change; she was sure of it. Little did she realize how drastically and tragically that change would be. That tonight would be the beginning of the end of her life.

Chapter 2

The smelter town of Anaconda is a short 25 miles west of Butte and about a third its size. The copper ore obtained from the Butte mines was shipped by rail on the BA&P (Butte, Anaconda, and Pacific) to the smelter in Anaconda. The smelting took the raw ore and, through a series of operations including a battery of converters, refined the ore by removing impurities through oxidation to a final product of approximately 99% pure copper.

Although viewed by some as the little brother of Butte, Anaconda offered much to the regional mining industry. Boasting the largest smokestack in the world, the residents of Anaconda were proud of their contribution. The stack was the tallest masonry structure in the world. Made primarily of brick with a concrete foundation and covered by a terra cotta coating, it had an overall height of 585 feet with 555 feet of chimney. Founded by Copper King Marcus Daly, Anaconda was a perfect complement to Butte's hill. As one made the trip from Butte, far in the distance, the stack was visible sitting on top of the hill outside of town. Billowing smoke drifted upward and easterly due to the prevailing winds. As you approached the town, large piles of black slag sat adjacent to the roadside. The slag, a byproduct of the smelting process, was odorless in its final cooled form, but during the process, the smell and taste of sulfur were strong and permeated the town and surrounding area. The smokestack, sitting high on the hill as though a sentinel watching guard, looking down on the little Smelter Town below. Small homes, tightly clustered on the east end of town, allowed for short travel to the smelter. The men working at the smelter were transported to and from work via a company street car. Bars were plentiful along the route, providing convenient and welcome refreshment as workers returned to town after a hard workday. Some estimated that Anaconda had more bars per capita than any place in the United States.

Theresa left her young daughter Jeanne and her son Raymond to be cared for by her mother, Mary, in Anaconda. Theresa did not have the resources, or interest for that matter, to care for her children. Thirteen-year-old Jeanne was a product of the first of four marriages. She and Nicholas Evans, her fourth, married two years before after a short relationship. He very reluctantly agreed to take on the children, but after a short time, Nick decided it was too much to care for children. He convinced Theresa that a move to Butte would be the start of a new life together. An opportunity to buy the Belmont Bar in uptown Butte presented itself and was too good an opportunity to pass up. Now, what to do with Jeanne and Raymond? Even if they had the resources, Theresa and Nick had little desire to be tied down. Their lifestyle was not conducive to raising children, especially now that operating a bar was in the picture.

Thankfully, you can rely on a grandmother's love. Jeanne missed her mother. She didn't understand why she was left behind and when, or if, her mother would return for her. Jeanne loved her grandmother but longed for the love and care of her mother, to feel wanted and valued. She had already had the disappointment of three father figures leaving her. Uncertainty and inconsistency filled her life. As a result, she often was withdrawn, finding getting close to anyone very difficult. She longed for love and consistency in her life, something she had experienced little in her young life. The closest had been with her grandmother Mary who had always been there for her. Now, more than ever, Jeanne needed her gramma to be there for her.

Relationships were not Theresa's strong point. Her first marriage to Charles Forster lasted eight years. It resulted in three children – including Jeanne; Marie Gertrude, who was five years older; and a brother, Lawrence, who died of spinal meningitis a month before Jeanne was born. A second marriage to Raymond Brown produced one child, Raymond Jr. They divorced after three years of marriage and Raymond Sr. died unexpectedly shortly afterwards. Her third marriage in January 1930 to William Robbins resulted in two more children, Patricia and Geraldine, and also ended in divorce and another failed relationship. It seemed Theresa was just not suited for marriage or motherhood

– and maybe for the children's sake, it was good she realized it. The only children she still had under her care were Jeanne and Raymond, but now she had left them to the attention of her mother in Anaconda while she pursued a life in Butte. Maybe, just maybe, she would return for them when she secured whatever it was that she sought.

Mary Harrington Green moved with her family from Michigan to Anaconda in 1898 when she was 13 years old. She was the oldest of 10 children, born when her mother was just 15 years old, and growing up she helped care for her younger siblings. She later married Fred Green, and together they had two sons and six daughters. She had spent most of her life caring for children, first her siblings, and later her own children. Now she was caring for her oldest daughter's children. It seemed caring for children was her lot in life.

"Gramma, when is momma coming back to get us?" Jeanne asked Mary.

"Jeanne, dear, we will be just fine right here."

"But she will come back, won't she, Gramma?"

Mary sighed, took a big breath. "We'll see, but now we will get along great together right here. I will always be here to love and care for you."

Mary turned away with tears in her eyes, knowing that Theresa likely was not coming back.

Chapter 3

Cork County Ireland
1935

The Irish potato famine, which began in 1845, had been very difficult for most families in Ireland. As a result of a fungus-like organism, the potato crops failed quickly, as the fungus spread rapidly. In the first year, one-quarter of the potato crop failed, and three-quarters were destroyed over the next seven years. As a result, one million Irish died during the famine due to starvation or related issues. Another million left Ireland as refugees by the time the famine ended in 1852. The famine led to large-scale immigration to America, though the desire to flee the British government's oppression was a factor as well.

By some estimates, 4.5 million Irish immigrated to the United States between 1820 and 1930. In 1940, they comprised nearly half of all immigrants to the United States. Initially, they came to cities like New York City and Boston, where they often faced discrimination because of their lack of skills. Most were listed as laborers since their background was principally farming. They were often looked down upon, and it was not unusual for employers to post signs that said, "No Irish need apply." Ellis Island's reception center opened on January 1, 1892, and approximately 12 million Irish passed through during the next 62 years.

Meanwhile, the discovery of metals in Butte, Montana, occurred. First, it was gold but not in large quantities, then silver. But it was copper that lifted Butte to prominence. By the turn of the century, Butte had become the world's largest copper mining town. With the birth of commercial electricity around the turn of the century, the demand for copper exploded, and Butte had large quantities under its hills. This required large numbers of miners and immigrants provided much of the need. Immigrants came from all over the world – Italians, Serbs, Croatians, Finns, Swedes, but none like the quantity of Irish. At the height of Butte's prosperity, it had a greater percentage of Irish as its population than any other city in the United States. At the turn of the century, one-quarter of Butte's population was of Irish descent. Ethnic diversity was so great that "no smoking" signs in the mines were in 16 different languages! Ethnic neighborhoods sprung up – Dublin Gulch for the Irish, Meaderville for the Italians, McQueen for Eastern Europeans, Finntown for the Scandinavians, and Williamsburg for Germans.

In America, there was the possibility of a new life full of opportunity. Many left for New York City, Boston, Philadelphia, and states across New England. Friends and family who had gone sent back word about the abundant jobs. Around the turn of the century, people began talking about the West. A man named Marcus Daly came talking about "The Richest Hill on Earth" and promised higher wages and opportunities if they would go west to Butte, Montana. He had discovered not gold as early settlers there sought but an abundance of copper ore. The increasing technology and expanding use of the telephone further increased the demand for copper ore. Copper for plumbing also drove the market and, therefore, prices. The opportunities at "The Richest Hill on Earth" had come to the people of Ireland!

The McCarthy family had been struggling for several years. Their potato farm had not survived the drought and famine. Brian McCarthy worked hard to provide for his family, working a variety of odd jobs where he could find them. But times were tough and getting tougher. When Marcus Daly came recruiting workers for his mines in America, Brian saw no choice but to move his family across the Atlantic to a new land, full of the promise of opportunity.

Michelle was the oldest of two McCarthy children. Now 17, she looked forward to the adventure of America. Her brother Eddie was ten. Michelle was given increased responsibility to care for her brother as both her mother and father had to work multiple jobs for survival; Michelle accepted the responsibility. Both parents working required them to be away from home for many hours a day, leaving Michelle to care for Eddie. Michelle loved her brother, but, at times, resented the heavy responsibility she had to bear. She longed to experience the life of a typical teenager.

Brian called the family together one summer evening. "I have some important and exciting news to share with all of you."

The children looked around at each other and their

mother. Eddie asked, "Are you going to have another baby?"

His mother, Elizabeth, laughed. "I certainly pray not."

"Did you find a new, good job, Father?" Michelle asked.

"Well, you might say that," replied Brian. "But...there is a catch."

After explaining that the work was in America, Eddie yelled in excitement, "What a great adventure! Wait, where is America, and how do we get there?"

However, Michelle became very quiet and looked away. Her mother watched her closely and noticed a tear running down her cheek. "What do you think, dear?" she asked.

"Momma, what about my friends and... Daniel?" Daniel was a boy she had met at school a few weeks ago and of whom she was very fond. "I don't want to leave my friends and especially Daniel. I know life is difficult here, and I know it is not going to get better anytime soon, but it will be tough to leave."

Elizabeth replied, "I know it will be difficult for us all, but the opportunities will be great, and besides, it doesn't mean we will be gone forever. Someday things in Ireland will improve, and we will return. We must look at this as a great adventure and opportunity!"

As the days passed, the McCarthy family prepared for their trip to America. There was much talk around town about the opportunities in America. Many neighbors had family and friends who had gone to America and wrote about job opportunities in the United States.

Though many remained in Boston or New York, a growing number ventured west due to mining job opportunities. So many Irish immigrants had moved to Butte that they formed their neighborhood, Dublin Gulch. The community sat on Butte Hill very near many of the mines. Here they could live near work and maintain much of the Irish heritage they treasured. The McCarthys felt a little less anxiety knowing a part of home awaited them in Butte.

The journey across the Atlantic was long and arduous. Most of the Irish immigrants were very poor. Typically, landlords in Ireland would kick renters to the street when they were no longer able to pay rent. However, it was not uncommon for landlords to pay to send the families across the Atlantic. They often made exaggerated promises of money, food and clothing and then pack them into overcrowded ships – often referred to as coffin ships because so many died from lack of food or disease. The 3000-mile journey could take 40 days to three months, depending on the vessel, weather, and skill of the captain. Often there was insufficient food and healthcare. Many were sick before ever leaving port. Some estimates suggest one in five passengers died from either malnutrition or disease due to the trip difficulty.

The McCarthys were very excited as the day of departure approached. Brian had heard stories of the poor conditions aboard ships, but his family's determination that they would safely make it to America encouraged him. Nevertheless, he chose not to share the stories with his family. He wanted them to remain excited and optimistic about their new journey ahead.

Fog and cold air greeted them as they arrived in the port town of Liverpool. The city was bustling with activity. Workers readied ships for travel, and fellow migrants were seemingly everywhere looking for a place to stay the night before the morning departure. Elizabeth McCarthy was overwhelmed.

"Brian, where will we find a place to stay? It is so crowded," she said. Brian had already been searching, but so far, no luck.

"Don't worry, Lizzie, surely there is somewhere for us to rest tonight."

The children were too excited to be concerned about a place to stay. Eddie was looking out over the pier at the ships and asked, "Which one is ours? I like the big one over there!"

Brian laughed, as Eddie was looking at a British Naval ship that was in port. Michelle said, "Eddie, don't be so silly. That is a navy ship. We will be in one of those ships over there."

On the other side of the harbor were several smaller ships, a few barely looking seaworthy. Elizabeth said, "Surely we are not traveling on one of those!"

Brian responded, "We will be fine whichever ship we are on as long as we are together and look out for each other."

With little money to their name and uncertainties ahead, Brian had to be very careful with how they spent their money. He decided that paying for a room in Liverpool was not feasible. Local inns were charging much more than usual because of the high demand. Brian found an area at the base of the cliffs where they would be protected from the wind. Although they had few supplies to bring on their journey, they had a few blankets to warm them from the cold night air. They brought along some dried fruit, a small amount of bread, and a few other food items they had gathered. It wasn't much but would get them through a few days, and then the ship's food should carry them through the remainder of the trip.

Eddie woke with a cough and complained that his throat was sore. Elizabeth was sure it was just a result of the night air. As the family gathered up their meager belongings, Michelle thought about her life ahead. She was leaving behind her friends and Daniel. Daniel's family, struggling to get by, were considering immigrating to America as well. Michele held onto the possibility that she and Daniel would someday reunite in America. She provided him all the information she had been able to gather regarding Butte and promised to write as soon as they arrived.

She told him, "I must be with my family and help them, but I long for us to be together again." Daniel had hugged her close, promising to find her in Butte if it was the last thing he did.

Crowds of people worked their way to the ships. Some carried suitcases, but most had small bags or just the clothing they wore and whatever they could bring in their arms. Brian searched for the ship they were assigned. He finally saw what he was looking for, the *SS Celtic*. The *Celtic* was an ocean liner built in 1872 and designed to carry passengers across the seas. It had seen better days but was still very seaworthy. Brian could see that the ship was already very crowded. He knew that the ships were often overcrowded because of demand, so he said to his family, "We must hurry, the ship is filling up fast, and we want to stake out a spot for us to be together." They hurried along, but Eddie's cough had worsened, and Elizabeth thought he was beginning to have a fever. Michelle carried Eddie while Brian and Elizabeth carried their few belongings. They could not help but be very excited, as people noisily prepared and said their goodbyes to family and friends. When they reached the gangway, there was hardly room to move because of the large number of travelers arriving. Eventually, after their papers were examined, they could embark. Once aboard, they realized that there were far too few cabins for the number of people aboard. After searching for space, they settled on an open area on a lower level of the ship where they could all be together. They had hoped for cabins with beds but had to settle for community space where they must sleep on the floor. But at least they were together and protected from the weather. Besides, they were all so excited about their prospects in America that nothing else seemed to matter.

Chapter 4

Plevan, Bulgaria
1932

Bulgaria in the late 1920s had been experiencing economic collapse. Two hundred thousand jobs were lost, and prices had dropped nearly 50% from the previous year. Dozens of companies had gone bankrupt. Per capita income was cut in half as the political system was in chaos. Fascism was taking over. Much of the collapse resulted from their disastrous involvement in World War I and the imposition of reparation payments. The economic collapse led to considerable discontent with the government. The onset of the worldwide Great Depression in 1929 produced further economic, social and political turmoil. Like much of Eastern Europe, Bulgarians struggled to survive; many were forced to go elsewhere to survive.

Nicholas Evanoff was 38 years old. Plevan, Bulgaria, had little to offer anyone trying to get ahead. He had worked a variety of labor jobs when he could find them, but the prospect for steady, good-paying employment was bleak. Opportunity in Bulgaria was reduced and not likely to improve in the foreseeable future. He had no formal training or education beyond secondary school, so his chances to improve were limited. His cousin Boris had worked in government for several years, but with the recent changes, he too was unable to find steady work in Plevan. Nearly a year ago, Boris had gone to America in search of opportunity. He had heard about the work opportunities in the Butte, Montana, mines from other Bulgarians who had relatives in America. He found work in the Alice Mine in Butte, and although the pay was good, conditions were dirty and risky.

In response to a letter from Nick, Boris offered him advice. "Conditions in the mine are dirty and, at times, quite dangerous. Daily we must rely on each other for safety and survival. The days are very long, and it is challenging to remain underground for hours at a time. Although the pay is good and opportunities are many, I advise against working in the mines. Rather, there are jobs available in nearby Anaconda at the smelter. Though the work is undoubtedly difficult and dirty, it is ABOVE ground, and the pay is comparable to the mines. If interested, reply soon, and I will inquire on your behalf."

"Papa and Mama, I have something important to tell you," said Nicholas. "As you know, conditions in Bulgaria are not good and getting worse. I have minimal opportunity here."

"This is true, son. But we are Bulgarians. We will endure and survive," his father replied.

"But I do not want just to survive. I have been thinking things over for a long time and have made a decision. I am going to America."

"America! Are you mad?" said his mama. "It is so far away, and your family is here."

"I know Mama, but I must look out for my future. I

have contacted cousin Boris, and he assured me I could find work there. I have made up my mind; I am leaving next Saturday."

His parents were devastated. Yet they knew things in Bulgaria were not good. Opportunities were so few.

"Mama, I know it is hard, but we must let him go. Nicholas is a grown man and needs to make his own choices. If that means going to America for a better opportunity, we must not stand in his way."

Through her tears, Mama nodded and turned away. There was nothing more she could say or do.

The journey to America was long and arduous. Travel from the small village of Plevan to the capital city of Sophia was easy, taking three hours to cover the 150 miles, with frequent stops along the way. Nicholas then boarded a train to Athens before his trans-Atlantic trip by ship to New York City. The trip was uneventful for the most part though exhausting and painfully slow. He had plenty of time to contemplate his future. How would he learn a new language? How would he deal with a different culture? Would he be welcomed? And most importantly, how would he manage to survive until he reached the Wild West of Montana? The closer he got to New York, the higher his anxiety grew.

Chapter 5

Anaconda, Montana
1938

After her divorce from William Robbins, Theresa had felt the need for some stability – and truth be known, she also needed some financial help. She had been living in San Bernardino, California, with Jeanne, Marie Gertrude, Raymond, Robbins, and their two daughters, but after they divorced, she knew she couldn't stay. Theresa knew living in California was not a viable plan for her, Jeanne, and Raymond, so she decided to return to Anaconda, leaving Robbins, their daughters, and Marie Gertrude behind. Living with her mother would give her a chance to get on her feet again. She and the children could hopefully live with Mary long enough to save money and make plans for their future. There were plenty of restaurant and bar jobs in Anaconda, and with Mary to help, she would be able to work at night.

The small house on East Sixth Street was barely big enough for the four of them. It had two small bedrooms, a small kitchen, a living room, and a closed-in porch. Theresa and Jeanne shared the second bedroom while Raymond slept on the sofa. The double bed took up nearly the entire space leaving little room for anything else. They shared a small closet and kept anything they didn't need daily out on the small enclosed porch. There was one small bathroom that they all shared. Space was tight and presented daily challenges to all of them.

"Mom," Theresa said to Mary one evening. "I appreciate your help with Jeanne and Raymond. I know it is challenging dealing with growing children in this small house."

"They are no problem," said Mary. "But I am concerned about all of you. You need to be more settled, more stable for all of your sakes."

"Please, Mother, don't start on me again. I am doing the best I can."

Mary replied, "Well, what is your plan for the future? You can't continue to jump from one man to another forever!"

Theresa turned away, slammed the door, and off she went. It was not like she had been trying to fail in her relationships. She wasn't even sure what it was she wanted. Security? Love? Companionship? Maybe she just needed frequent change. But at this point, it was clear that what she had been doing was not working. She was nearly penniless, and there was nothing to suggest things were going to change anytime soon. Working nights at the Owl Bar was not going to get them ahead. Most jobs in Anaconda were low paying, except for the smelter. But most smelter jobs were not suitable for a woman. There must be a better way, she thought.

Turning west on Third Street, Theresa contemplated her future. As she approached the city Commons, activity significantly increased. Over at the nearby Washoe Theatre, people had gathered for the evening showing of the Marx Brothers movie, *A Day at the Races*. An art deco building, the theater was universally considered the most beautiful building in Anaconda. Situated on Main Street across from the Commons, it marked the beginning of the business district. Dotted with multiple bars and shops, Anaconda was busy that night. Theresa headed north on Main from Third Street toward Thompson's Bar which was across the street from the elegant Montana Hotel. The crisp evening air blew onto her neck, making her wish she had brought a scarf. The sidewalk was bustling with people enjoying the evening. Some were shopping in the local family-owned businesses. The JC Penney store anchored downtown while small clothing stores, a candy store, a jewelry store, a barbershop, a sporting goods store, and the Anaconda Company Store lined Main street near Thompson's.

Approaching the bar, Theresa suddenly heard shouting. Out the front door came several men surrounding two men who were throwing punches at one another. The first tumbled to the ground, as the second man jumped on top of him. The crowd that had gathered was cheering them on with no one attempting to break up the fight. Blood dripped from the first man's nose while the other had a gash on his chin.

"All right, boys, that's enough for tonight," said a voice from behind Theresa. Sgt. Sullivan had seen this play out so many times before; excessive drinking after a hard day at work, someone gets offended by something someone else says, and off they go with fisticuffs. "You boys had better just relax and shake hands, or someone is going to get hurt. And then I will have to haul both of you to jail to cool off a bit. Now, nobody wants that, so let's just break it up."

Theresa watched intently. There was something about the second man that intrigued her. During the fight, he spoke with a very unusual accent. She couldn't quite place it, but it was slightly different from what she had heard around Anaconda before. With the ethnic diversity of the smelter workers, she was used to hearing Irish, Italian, German and Scandinavian accents. It sounded similar to the Croatians she knew, but a bit different, and something about it was very attractive to her. As the crowd dispersed back into the bar, the man was left alone. It was apparent that most people were supporting the other man in the fight.

"Do you need any help?" she said to him as he leaned against the building. The man started to respond in anger, but when he looked up and saw Theresa, he smiled and said in his broken English, "I could use a hand getting to my feet."

Theresa gave him her arm and guided him to his feet.

"Thank you, ma'am," the stranger replied, wiping the blood off his face on the sleeve of his shirt. Theresa pulled out her handkerchief from her purse and helped wipe away the blood.

"What was that all about?"

The man shook his head and answered, "Apparently, the locals don't take well to strangers sometimes. I have only recently come to town and thought I would get to know some folks, but I guess a bar full of drunks is not the best way to meet people."

"How long have you been here, in Anaconda, I mean?" Theresa asked.

"I arrived yesterday, looking for work. I heard that there are good-paying jobs at the smelter, so I am hoping to find work there".

"Where are you from? I don't recognize your accent."

"It's a long story, ma'am."

"Well, I have plenty of time."

An hour later, Theresa and Nick Evans – changed from Evanhoff when he arrived in New York – were still sipping coffee at the Park Cafe. She was attracted to his accent and fascinated by his story. She thought he was brave and adventurous to have left his home country and make his way to Montana. He told her how he arrived in New York City with very little money and unable to speak English. He knew there would be opportunities in New York and that there would be fellow Bulgarians there to help him navigate a whole new world. He told of the difficulty finding fellow Bulgarians in the large city, the hard life of living and working in a city of such diversity and high level of competition for work. He talked about the genuine dislike each group seemed to have for the others – likely a combination of many factors including competition for work, looking out for "their own," prejudice that developed as a result of the recent world war, and the political upheaval extending in Europe and elsewhere. The increasing political upheaval only fueled those feelings, and many felt that another war was imminent.

Theresa watched Nick with fascination and felt she could listen to him for hours. Between his story and the accent with which he spoke, she found herself drawn to this man in a way that she couldn't explain. She had only just met him, yet she felt powerfully drawn to him. It might be that she was too quickly attracted to men – as evidenced by her previous three husbands – but she felt this was much different.

Nick continued to share how he found work in New York City at a loading dock. Unloading ships of cargo from Europe and elsewhere was hard work but paid pretty well. And with his limited English, it was a good fit. He explained how he worked there for nearly two years and gradually learned enough English to get by. He also was able to put away some money, knowing that he did not want to stay in the city long term. He told her about his cousin Boris in Butte and how he had offered to help him find work in the Butte-Anaconda area if he were able to make it out west. He shared how he decided a couple of months before that he should come west for work. He had saved enough money to pay for the journey and a little extra to get by for a couple of weeks until he could find work. The trip from New York City to Butte was long, traveling by train to Minneapolis, then through North Dakota and eastern Montana, and finally arriving in Butte. He spent a couple of weeks in Butte with Boris. The day before, he came to Anaconda hoping to find work at the smelter. The next day, he would meet with those responsible for hiring and hopefully become a "smelterman."

"So that is pretty much my story in America," Nick finished.

Theresa responded, "That is an amazing journey. You are brave to leave your country and come to a land you don't know. I admire you for that."

Theresa and Nick exited the Park Cafe, headed east on Park Street, and then south on Cherry Street to avoid passing by Thompson's Bar again. He had offered to walk her back to her mother's home. After turning east on Third Street, they walked to Birch then south to Sixth Street, and soon they were in front of the house.

"Will I get to see you again?" Evans asked.

"I certainly hope so," replied Theresa. With that, Theresa turned to go inside and noticed her mother watching out the window. Mary had been thinking about their earlier argument. Maybe I was too hard on her, she had been thinking, but now she could only shake her head and turn away. She had seen this pattern before, but maybe, hopefully, this time, things will be different.

Chapter 6

Atlantic Ocean

The long trip across the Atlantic was proving to be more difficult than Brian McCarthy had expected. Keeping his family safe and together was his primary goal. The ship was large, and sharing space with others challenging. Arguments over space and food/water seemed to happen daily. Patience was wearing thin, as the days were long, and time dragged on slowly. Young Eddie's cough was getting worse with each passing day. After several days of nearly nonstop coughing, Brian was able to locate a doctor on the ship to examine Eddie.

"Mr. McCarthy, I am afraid the news isn't good. Eddie is very ill. He has whooping cough or Bordetella pertussis," said Dr. Owens.

He explained that Bordetella pertussis was a result of highly infectious bacteria damaging the tiny hairs within airways called cilia. The impact was a persistent dry cough since the cilia are not efficiently removing particulate. It was highly contagious for several weeks and spread via contact with body fluids. Children are particularly vulnerable. Eddie likely was infected a few days before boarding the ship. As it progressed, it resulted in chills, runny nose, headaches, and low-grade fever – all of which Eddie demonstrated.

"Surely, it is treatable. Eddie will be all right, won't

he? Brian asked pleadingly.

Dr. Owens expressed concern since the symptoms had progressed so rapidly. He recommended treatment with antibiotics and isolation from others, but admittedly the supply was minimal on the ship. Besides, at Eddie's stage, their effectiveness was greatly diminished. And isolation was nearly impossible on an overly crowded boat.

"I will do everything I can for him, but I am constrained. Time is of the essence. If he can hold on until we get to New York, we can get him better care than I can provide."

Brian and Elizabeth paced the floor but neither said anything. Each knew the gravity of the situation. Dr. Owens insisted Eddie be isolated as much as possible from the other passengers though he knew that others were likely already exposed. After meeting with ship officials, they vacated a small cabin for Eddie. The family could now only wait to see if he would respond to the antibiotics.

"Brian, his cough is getting worse by the day," Elizabeth exclaimed.

"I know, and his fever is increasing as well. He needs better care than can be provided on the ship, but we are still several days from arriving in New York City," Brian replied.

"I just hope there is enough time..." Elizabeth trailed off.

The seas grew rougher as they approached the eastern seaboard of the United States. Eddie was barely able to eat and slept when he wasn't coughing. He had lost significant weight from his already tiny frame. Elizabeth woke after dozing off for a short while.

"Brian, I need some fresh air and to stretch. I am going to take a walk on deck."

As she walked along, she noticed a few people excitedly pointing in the distance. In the far distance, peering across the sea was the faint outline of Lady Liberty. A sense of excitement rose in her, but it lasted only a brief moment. It was replaced by a sense of dread, knowing how ill her child was and the grave nature of his condition. Yet, she held out hope now, knowing they were nearing New York City and better medical care.

The Statue of Liberty arrived at Bedloe's Island on June 19, 1885. At 151 feet high, she had come to symbolize liberty, freedom and democracy. It was a gift from the people of France to the American people; she was beloved by nearly everyone and particularly revered by the immigrants arriving from all over Europe to seek a new life of opportunity, freedom and safety.

As word spread aboard ship, people were rushing to the decks to get their first look. Some were crying, others cheering, while still others were feeling the anxiety of what lay in store for them. For most, it was a dream come true, an opportunity to leave behind the things that made life nearly unbearable. Some were fleeing poverty, others oppression. Many left behind a past that they would simply rather forget. This was a chance to start a new life.

After a few minutes of taking in the view, Elizabeth hurriedly returned to the cabin to share the good news with her family. But just as she reached the cabin door, she was met by Brian.

"I must find the doctor quickly. Eddie is worsening and unresponsive."

When Elizbeth looked over to the bed and saw Eddie, she screamed out. "No, hold on, my darling little boy, we are so close." She cradled him in her arms, desperately trying to get some response from him. "God, please don't take my son from me!" But there was very little response from Eddie. His coughing had all but ceased, his breathing was very shallow, and his forehead felt as though it was on fire. *Hurry Brian,* she pleaded, if only to herself.

Just then, Brian arrived with Dr. Owens. After examining him, the doctor said, "I am afraid it doesn't look good. There is nothing more I can do."

Brian prayed, "Hold on, my son." Surely there was more advanced treatment in New York City, if he could just hold on a little while longer.

The ship bustled with activity in preparation for landing at Ellis Island. Crew members were preparing the boat for docking, and passengers were gathering up their belongings. The excitement was palpable. Brian had left to see if he could expedite obtaining medical care for their young son. The doctor had made an urgent request to the ship's officers to get the McCarthy's to the front of the line to disembark. Brian hurried back to the cabin to deliver the news, but as he entered, he saw Elizabeth in the corner holding the now lifeless Eddie...and sobbing.

Chapter 7

Cabby Young had spent his entire life in Butte. His grandfather immigrated from England nearly 70 years before and came to Butte to work in the mines. When he arrived, Butte was a mining camp, not officially established as a town until 1864. Like many others of the time, the promise of gold in the area attracted him. The most abundant mineral found was copper, though, and he decided to stay and make his fortune. Quickly the local mines were taken over by the large mining companies, so he eventually became an employee of the Amalgamated Copper Company. Cabby's father followed his father's footsteps, working in the mines for several years before being killed in the 1917 Speculator Mine fire – a disaster that claimed the lives of 168 miners. It was the worst mining disaster in Butte's history. The fire broke out in the lower levels of the mine, presumably from a broken power cable that carried power to the underground pumps. The lower levels of the shafts quickly filled with smoke and gas, the fire then spreading to the Diamond Mine. Four hundred fifteen men worked the night shift in the Speculator, and 213 escaped through other shafts, but the remainder were trapped inside. Rescue efforts took place for several days, but few were saved. Cabby's father was one of the unlucky who perished underground.

Cabby decided that day that he would never work in the mines. Instead, he had bounced around a variety of service jobs in Butte. He settled on being a cook and had worked many restaurants in Butte, including his current position at the M & M Cafe. Although work as a cook was easy to find, it didn't pay particularly well.

Business was slow that morning at the M & M. Standing at the grill looking out the window at the traffic on Main Street, Cabby considered his life in Butte. His white work shirt was covered in grease and food stains, reminding him of the limited opportunity his job provided. He was lost in his thoughts when he was interrupted by a voice behind him.

"How does a guy get service in this place?" asked the man on the counter's other side.

"We generally don't serve people like you," Cabby said through a grin.

The man was unshaven and looked like he was in desperate need of some sleep. His hair was uncombed, and his monogrammed shirt read *Maloney's Bar*. At 6-foot-2 and 250 pounds, he was an imposing sight. Yet his broad smile and easy-going personality made him likable to all who met him. Ed Deanne and Cabby Young had become friends years ago, from the time they met in junior high school.

"You look awful! Long night?" chided Young.

"Yeah, haven't even been home yet. I could use a little breakfast."

They visited over breakfast since there were no other

customers. "There has got to be a better way to make a living than cooking and bartending," said Deanne. "It's hard to get ahead."

"I agree. Working in the mines is about the only way to make good money around here. But there is no way I am going to work underground. There are ways to supplement income, however," Cabby said with a sly grin.

Cabby was always looking for ways to supplement his income. Sometimes that involved legal avenues, sometimes not so legal. He frequented the many bars, always looking for a card game to make some extra cash. At times, when gambling wasn't particularly profitable, he turned to shady methods such as theft or performing various "jobs" for others that needed doing – ultimately leading him into a relationship with Milo Ivankovich, owner of the Empire Hotel. Ivankovich also managed several cribs and other single rooms around Butte to rent out. Of course, payment was always under the table, and sometimes renters needed a little encouragement to make payment. That was where Cabby often came in. It was a reasonably quick way to make some extra money, though it was a bit dangerous. Most of the renters were women, but that didn't necessarily make it easy for him. They could be desperate, and desperation can be hazardous. Cabby would be contacted by Ivankovich, who would give him the name and address of the delinquent renter. He would then pay a visit to the offender and apply whatever pressure was necessary to obtain payment.

Sometimes the renter would plead to be given a few more days to come up with the money, as they often simply didn't have the cash. Cabby used these times as opportunities for his further benefit. Utilizing loan sharks, Cabby would offer to loan the women money to make their rent. He would act as a middle man between the two and receive a modest fee for his troubles. Of course, it was a little risky for him if the renter did not make a payment, as the shark came after Cabby. He learned how to play the game and always seemed to remain one step ahead.

"I know about some of your supplemental income jobs," replied Deanne. "But they are a bit too risky for me. You've got to do what you've got to do, but those jobs are not for me."

As a result of the many business activities Cabby was involved with, he became well known to many in Butte. His reputation in the city frequently led to additional opportunities for making quick cash. It was this reputation that prompted Ivankovich to seek out his services. He knew that having Cabby to employ would be fruitful in more ways than one.

Deanne was aware of Cabby's dealings with Ivankovich but wanted nothing to do with them. "Be careful, Cabby. Those types of people don't fool around. Watch your back and don't get in over your head."

Chapter 8

Anaconda, Montana

Theresa and Nick had been seeing each other regularly now. He was able to find work on the smelter as a laborer or "smelterman." The work was dirty and dangerous at times, but it paid well with labor wages recently increasing to an all-time high of $5.25 per day as a result of the price of copper rising. And, most importantly, the work was above ground. Nick was thrilled to have a good-paying job considering the deteriorating economy he left behind in Bulgaria. His salary was considerably more than he could ever make in Bulgaria. There indeed were opportunities in America.

Smelting was a lengthy process of applying heat and chemicals to extract metals from ore. It removed many types of metal, but in Anaconda's case – copper. The process decomposed the raw ore, driving off elements as gas and slag, leaving the minerals behind. The low-grade ore was then concentrated by crushing and separating the heavier metal from the other particles. Copper concentrates then were roasted in large furnaces, called roasters, to remove sulfur and then smelted in a blast or reverberatory furnace to further remove impurities. The result was a hot molten copper and slag, a waste material made of silica, black sand, and iron oxide. The residue was cooled, and the molten copper then processed in converter furnaces. This "blister" copper was further refined in cast furnaces and eventually made into anodes and shipped to Great Falls. The process left behind mounds of black slag and the taste of sulfur in the air around Anaconda.

Nick's job was to assist in Roaster #2. This roaster consisted of huge ovens for drying before being sent to the arsenic roaster, then the "reverb" (another set of furnaces which turned it into a molten liquid). Then, onto the converter. It was a scorching environment created by hot air to break down the ore. In addition to being very hot, his job involved handling very heavy molten liquid, manually stirring the roaster contents (called rabbling), and exposure to dangerous chemicals (especially sulfur dioxide and arsenic). It was not a very glamorous job, and not a job he wanted to do long term, but it paid well and allowed him to put some money away.

Theresa continued to work as a waitress at the Montana Hotel Cafe during the day and part-time as a barmaid at the Owl Bar at night. They were not ideal jobs for her, but they paid her bills and provided for her, Jeanne, and Raymond, with Mary's help. But life in Anaconda was not what she had dreamed. She had visions of something bigger and better, something that would allow her more independence and the ability to make more money. She felt trapped. Opportunities were few for a woman with children, and she didn't like having to live with her mother. Though she was grateful, finances limited her significantly. Antsy, she began looking for better opportunities.

Nick, too, was getting tired of his job and desired something better. Sure, there was opportunity within the Anaconda Copper Company to advance, but it would still involve dirty and dangerous work, something he didn't want long term. Nick had visions of being more independent, maybe owning a business, and making his way on his terms. He and Theresa often talked about their dreams for something better.

Theresa awoke to a brilliant blue sky, except for the plume of smoke hovering directly above the large stack. She felt the warm sunshine coming through her bedroom window. It was a near windless day. The air over Anaconda, however, tasted strongly of the sulfur emanating from the stack. It was a rare day when both Nick and Theresa had the day off together.

"Let's get out of town, it's such a pretty day," Theresa said to Nick.

"Great idea. Where would you like to go?"

"Today would be a great day to drive up to Georgetown Lake for a picnic. We can spend the afternoon enjoying the lake and talking about our future."

Beautiful Georgetown Lake was fifteen miles west of Anaconda, a man-made reservoir created by a dam of Flint Creek, a creek descending from the Pintlar Mountains west toward Phillipsburg. Sitting at 6,425 feet elevation, the lake expands over 3700 acres. Established initially for power production in 1885, it soon functioned primarily for recreation and providing water to valley farmers. Nestled between the Sapphire, Pintlar, and Flint Creek mountain ranges, it was a beautiful escape from the everyday stresses of life. It was the perfect spot for Theresa and Nick to get away and contemplate their life together and what may lie ahead.

Theresa spread out a blanket on the grass at Denton's Point near the lakeshore. The menu consisted of fried chicken, potato salad, a couple of apples, and a few Olympia beers.

They had been seeing each other often the past few weeks and enjoyed each other's company. Theresa considered talking to Nick about her dissatisfaction with her job and her desire for more, but the day seemed so perfect she didn't want to risk spoiling it. The blue sky, mild breeze over the lake, and the peacefulness were almost too much to take in. Theresa decided now was not the time to discuss her dissatisfaction with her job. She didn't want to spoil what turned out to be a perfect day. She found herself falling for this man.

Chapter 9

New York City

The McCarthys arrived distraught in New York City at Castle Garden Wharf in lower Manhattan. They had lost the youngest member of the family to whooping cough only days before. Nearly all of the excitement and optimism they shared when they left Ireland was gone. They left a land of poverty with little opportunity to come to an area rich in opportunity, but now they felt nothing but loss. Brian, Elizabeth, and Michelle disembarked from the ship with hundreds of fellow immigrants to a land they didn't know, feeling helpless and hopeless.

Castle Garden pier was on the southern tip of Manhattan Island and served as a disembarkation point for the thousands of immigrants arriving from Europe. The once busy industrial area soon became a slum area for immigrants who arrived with very little – sometimes just the satchels on their backs. They came gaunt and weak from the long trip, sharing stories of the horrific disease-ridden journey across the Atlantic to anyone who would listen. Typically, the new arrivals were met by people from their homeland who had lived in New York City for some time. Known as "immigrant runners," their job was to help those arriving find boarding houses, soup kitchens, and other necessities. There was a cost, however. In exchange for help, the expectation was that the immigrants sign over their voting cards and pledge support to the local political factions that paid the runners. This practice helped feed the political machine and frequently resulted in the formation of ethnic gangs. It was through these gangs that many immigrants survived and were protected.

The Irish were the first to establish gangs in Manhattan and had the largest membership. Of course, they had the most significant number of immigrants arriving, but the Italians, Eastern Europeans, Germans, and the native-born Americans formed gangs as well.

The area, typically referred to as Five Points, was a reference to the convergence of Canal, Bowery, Chatham, Pearl, and Centre Streets. These formed a triangular area known as Paradise Square. It was here where gangs often congregated and turf battles fought. The neighborhood was also near the slums, where many immigrants began their journey in America.

"Brian how are we going to find a place to stay and food to eat? There are so many getting off the ships, and all needing food and shelter. It is so overwhelming," Elizabeth exclaimed with worry in her voice.

"Don't worry; we will be all right. Surely there are people who can help us. People arrive on the ships nearly every day, so certainly there is help."

Hungry and tired, they looked around, hoping to find someone to give them some help. The streets were overcrowded, and people were shouting at one another. Patience was running thin, and people who were excited hours ago felt anxious and desperate. As the

McCarthy's walked away from the pier toward the city, they lost all feelings of optimism. The excitement they shared when leaving Ireland gave way to anxiety, fear and sadness from the recent loss of Eddie.

"All right there, bud?" came a voice from the doorway as they passed by. "You look like you could use a helping hand."

Brian turned to see a young Irishman extending his outstretched hand. "Michael Moriarity, at your service."

"We just arrived from the ship and have nowhere to stay tonight. We are hungry and thirsty. We could surely use some help."

"Come with me then," replied the young man. "I can show you a place to get a meal and a place to stay for a few nights."

Distraught and overwhelmed, Brian was thankful for the offer of assistance. They gathered the few things they possessed and followed the runner to the dilapidated buildings that served as already overcrowded housing for immigrants. Few had been able to move on from Five Points, and so overcrowding worsened as the weeks and months passed. The runner took them to a makeshift soup kitchen that had very meager supplies but a very welcome sight to the McCarthys.

Though they were appreciative, within a short time Brian realized there was a cost to receiving help from the runner. Soon he was instructed in the process of supporting the Irish mobsters via his vote. They expected that he would cast his vote for the Irish politicians, their surrogates, or a price paid.

New York City and the Five Points area was a tough place to survive without the help of the local gangs. It was either accept their support and work with the system or risk survival. The Prohibition era of the 1920s and early 1930s was a challenging and often dangerous time. Irish gangs had infiltrated the city with an ever-increasing influence on politics and the police force. Bootlegging was a very prosperous business for the mobsters, and having the politicians and police in their pocket was essential. As the Jazz Age had progressed, the Irish dominated the police force and politics. Mobsters such as John Morrisey, Tim Sullivan, Danny Driscoll, Trigger Burke, Eddie "The Butcher" Cummiskey, Eddie and Jack Diamond, Mickey Spillane, Red Rocks Farrell, Googy Corcoran, Slops and Baboon Connelly, Owney Madden, Mad Dog Coll, and Two-Gun Frank Crowley made their mark on the city. They had turned bootlegging into a very lucrative lifestyle using bribery, violence, and murder to intimidate anyone who dared stand in their way.

But it wasn't just the Irish. Italians, Poles, Germans, and many other ethnic groups formed formidable gangs as well. The Irish were the first and the most dominant, but over time the Italians would gradually force out the Irish. For now, the Irish mobsters had control. They called the shots, and the survival of new Irish immigrants depended on cooperation with the mob for their protection.

Initially, Brian found finding work very difficult in

New York City. He worked some odd jobs but was barely making enough for his young family to survive.

"What are we going to do?" Elizabeth asked Brian. "We barely have enough to eat, and we need to find a suitable place to live. There is so much disease here; it is not good for us to remain. We already have lost one child."

"I know," Brian replied. "There are so many here looking for work, but there are few opportunities for us Irish. So many places that I have checked have posted signs that say Irish need not apply. I don't know what to do."

So far, he had been able to distance himself from the gangsters and their bootlegging operations. But times were getting more desperate.

Chapter 10

Butte, Montana

Detective Duggan was well aware of the Empire Hotel and much of what took place there. Its location next to Pleasant Alley and the brothels tended to attract Butte's undesirables. Rooms had become relatively cheap, and many who had sketchy pasts lived here. Sure, there were those trying to make it who just needed an affordable place to stay temporarily. There were single women who were working low-paying jobs but hoped to work their way up financially. But there also were women who were there to take advantage of the many men willing to pay for sexual services nearby. And some have had issues with the law, alcohol, drugs, or bad financial decisions. Duggan and the police force had been called frequently to the Empire for a variety of reasons. As a result, they regularly monitored the area to deter illegal activity. But it was a difficult task. With limited resources and a general acceptance by the community for much of the "business" taking place, the job was very challenging. It had become an acceptable way of life for the miners and overlooked by most in the community. Still, Duggan and his staff kept a close eye on the Empire and the surrounding area.

The temperature began to cool as the summer sun dropped below the horizon. A typical time for activity around the Dumas Brothel and Pleasant Alley to pick up,

Duggan decided to visit the area. Turning the corner from Wyoming onto Mercury Street, he walked past the front of the Dumas. Both patrons and the ladies were used to seeing police around, but they were undeterred. They knew full well that prostitution was acceptable in Butte, though technically not legal. In fact, the ladies welcomed the occasional police presence. They knew it helped deter theft and other illegal activity.

"Hey there, detective," came a voice from a second-story window of the Dumas.

Looking up, Duggan saw a woman in a bright red dress. Excessively made up, her dress quite short, and both shoulders uncovered. "You look a little stressed, care to come up for a visit?" she asked. Walking on, Duggan just smiled and shook his head.

Reaching the corner, he turned north on Main Street and then entered the alley between Mercury and Galena Streets. To the locals, this was known as Pleasant Alley, for apparent reasons. It sometimes was referred to as Venus Alley, so named for the rear entrance to the Dumas Brothel. That night it was pretty quiet, but the evening was young. Scanning the rear of the two-story Dumas, he observed the double-decker cribs, each illuminated by a single white bulb and a young lady in varying levels of undress. Most were leaning over their crib toward the alley in an effort to attract men passing by. Duggan surmised that none of them have been successful yet tonight.

Continuing down Pleasant Alley toward Wyoming Street, Duggan reached the rear of the Empire Hotel.

Though not officially a brothel, its location provided cheap rooms for some girls to live when they were not working. Indeed, not all who lived there were prostitutes, but they were well aware of the activity around them. It tended to attract a particular element that Duggan was always concerned about, those who were willing to take advantage of the girls or their patrons by illegal means. Whether by thievery, drug dealing, or extortion, there was an element for which Duggan always was on the watch. As he turned the corner of the building onto Galena Street, one such person caught his eye. Just entering the Empire Hotel was its owner, Milo Ivankovich.

Ivankovich was well-known to Duggan. The police force frequently watched him, as they knew full well that some of Ivankovich's dealings were shady if not outright illegal. He was suspected of promoting prostitution, drug trafficking, and exploitation, but hard evidence had been hard to come by. He had been very good at covering his tracks and using others to do his dirty work. Duggan had been looking for months to catch Ivankovich in his illegal activity, but so far, Ivankovich had remained a step ahead. He was smart enough to find others to do his dirty work and keep his hands clean. But Duggan was sure Ivankovich was behind much of the illegal activity. He just needed to prove it. Duggan was also aware of Ivankovich's association with Cabby Young, so he was keeping an eye on him as well.

Just a few months ago, one of the Empire's tenants

disappeared without a trace. Duggan surmised that she had failed to pay a portion of her fees to Ivankovich and that he had her "taken care of" by one of his hired men. Duggan suspected it was Young, but no evidence so no arrest. Questioned on several occasions, both Ivankovich and Young had solid alibis. Still, Duggan remained convinced they both were involved. Ivankovich had others he had hired to do his dirty work, but he always seems to protect himself from being implicated. Duggan knew it was only a matter of time before he slipped up.

A few minutes later, Duggan saw Young turning the corner in a hurry and walking toward the Empire. Looking up, Young saw Duggan in front of the Empire's Galena Street entrance.

"Good evening Young. You look like you are in a hurry to get somewhere, it must be important," said Duggan.

"Uh, just meeting up with someone," he stammered in surprise.

"Wouldn't be Ivankovich, would it?"

"Umm... no sir. I have a lady friend who lives here. Just going to visit her."

"Well, that's quite a coincidence because I just saw Ivankovich go inside. I am thinking you two have some business to discuss."

"I didn't even know he was here. I am just going to see my friend."

"Maybe you could introduce me to your friend then," suggested Duggan.

"I don't think she would have much interest in meeting a policeman," replied Young.

"I suspect not. And I don't suppose Ivankovich wants to meet with me tonight either."

"You would have to ask him."

"Maybe I will. And maybe I'll ask about your meeting."

"I told you, I don't have a meeting with him tonight."

It didn't get by Duggan that Young said tonight. "My advice, Young – don't get involved with Ivankovich any night. He is bad news, and you'll only get into trouble that you won't be able to get out of."

Chapter 11

Anaconda, Montana

"Theresa, have you ever considered owning and operating a business?" Nick asked.

"Not really," she responded. "I don't have the education or knowledge for running a business. And besides, where would I come up with the money?"

"I have been investigating, and I think I have found a great opportunity for us."

"For us?"

"Yes, for *us*. I have been able to put away some money, and I am sure we can borrow a little more."

Stunned, Theresa asked, "What kind of business?"

"I have been inquiring around, and there is a bar for sale in Butte. The current owner is willing to take us on as operators/managers until we can come up with the remaining money for a down payment. The price is reasonable, and the location is excellent. It is near the uptown business district and mines, so it is a prime spot for the miners. I have looked over the books, and the bar has been able to make a modest profit this year, but there is potential to make much more. Nearly every year since Prohibition ended, the bar has been more profitable. The owner is also willing to pay us to manage the bar until we can come up with the down, and then we can take over! "

Theresa was shocked but intrigued. This might be the

opportunity she has been hoping for. A chance to make some decent money, be more independent, and the opportunity to leave Anaconda. Sure, Jeanne and Raymond would have to stay with her mother, but she thought that would be only temporary. Once the bar was doing well, she would be able to come for them. Surely her mother wouldn't mind. Theresa knew her mother was concerned about her future, so she would certainly understand the opportunity this presented for her, wouldn't she? Theresa tried to convince herself yet dreaded breaking the news to her mother and the children. But this was an opportunity she could not turn down.

"Mom, kids, I have something very important to tell you. I know that the news is likely to surprise you, and probably disappoint you, but I have made an important decision about my future."

Mary raised an eyebrow and Jeanne apprehensively asked, "what are you talking about? What kind of decision?"

Before Mary could say anything, Theresa told them, "I have decided to move to Butte with Nick. He has found a great business opportunity for us. We are going to operate the Belmont Bar and if all goes well, in a few months we will purchase it."

Mary stood there shaking her head. "What are you thinking? You aren't married to Nick and haven't you learned anything from your other relationships? Besides, you don't know the first thing about running a business and my guess is he doesn't either."

"This IS different. Nick and I have spent a lot of time together and we are in love. Besides, we have both spent a lot of time around bars and I have worked in a few. We are confident we can make this work," replied Theresa.

"Working in a bar is nothing like owning one. Neither of you have a business background and Nick will be giving up a very solid, stable job. Two single people running a business is too risky," Mary responded.

"Well, I have some additional news. Nick and I are going to get married."

Jeanne looked at her mother in disbelief. "Mother, you can't. I like school here and am making excellent grades. I have good friends and am looking forward to attending St. Peter's High School in a few years. We can't leave and go to Butte," she pleaded.

Looking over at Mary, Theresa said, "That's the thing. I can't take you and Raymond with us right now. Nick and I will come to get you after we get the business going well. Besides, it is only 30 miles away. Mom, I need you to look after Jeanne and Raymond until we are able to bring them to Butte to live with us."

Mary responded, "I can't believe you are planning to do this? You have known each other less than a year! You just continue your repeatable pattern of poor choices with men and I don't see this being any different."

Of course, Mary would care for the children. She knew the children would need her now more than ever.

Tears filled Jeanne's eyes. She had only recently

begun to feel a sense of security and love from her mother.

"Mother, why are you doing this to us? I don't want you to leave," Jeanne said.

"Don't worry, I will be back to get you just as soon as we get settled and the bar is ours. Then you can come live with us in Butte."

"But I don't want to move to Butte" Jeanne said through tears. "I like it here with Gramma and my friends."

"We can talk about that later. Gramma will take good care of you, and I will visit often."

***

Two weeks later, Theresa and Nick said their vows at the Deer Lodge County Courthouse before the Justice of the Peace with Mary and Theresa's sister Ursula attending as witnesses. It had been a small, simple ceremony with just family in attendance. After all, it was her fourth wedding. Other than his cousin Boris who came over from Butte, Nick had no family present since the others lived in Bulgaria. Theresa had a couple of sisters attend and, of course, Jeanne and Raymond.

The county courthouse was a beautiful building with a copper dome at its apex. It sat at the south end of Main Street. The date was January 28, 1938, and heavy snow had been falling all day. The white-coated Ponderosa Pine trees surrounding the courthouse provided a beautiful setting. Travel from the courthouse down Main Street proved to be a bit tricky. The heavy snow and gradual decline made travel a little slow, but as the wedding party reached the city commons, the bright lights of the forty-five foot tall Christmas tree illuminated the entire area. The tree was provided annually by the Anaconda Copper Company to the citizens of Anaconda. The commons were then flooded by the fire department to create a large ice skating rink for everyone. The enclosed warming shed provided relief for the skaters when conditions proved too cold.

The Croatian Hall on East Third Street was beautifully decorated for the reception. In typical Anaconda fashion, the wedding reception had plenty of food, drink, music and dancing. While family and friends celebrated until the early morning hours with Theresa and Nick, Mary had taken Jeanne and Raymond home hours ago. They hadn't felt like celebrating. Life was about to change once again for them.

Mary was about the only stable figure in Jeanne's life. Marie Gertrude married her stepfather, William Robbins, and remained in California with Jeanne's half-sisters Geraldine and Patricia. Raymond, her half-brother, would live with Jeanne and Mary. She had some aunts, uncles, and cousins in Anaconda, but they were not particularly close. Right now, she felt like Gramma Mary was the only one who loved her and was concerned about her. As soon as the reception ended, Theresa and Nick would move to Butte, and Jeanne and Raymond would be left behind with their grandmother.

Chapter 12

New York City

Bootlegging had become a very lucrative business in New York City since Prohibition. The Irish were increasingly taking more prominent roles in local government and police work and in the bootlegging business. The immigrants in lower Manhattan had begun taking on these roles for sheer survival. The Irish mob controlled much of the local bootlegging operations and regularly recruited immigrants to expand their territory. The newly arriving Irish immigrants were easy targets. They were very poor and desperate for work. Most of them were brought into the fold with seemingly safe, legal jobs. But once they demonstrated that they were consistent and reliable workers, they were often moved into illegal bootlegging. It was not easy to resist the mob if they wanted you. Intimidation and threats were used on the worker and his family if there was any resistance. The mob needed workers to move their illegal products and typically didn't take no for an answer to a job offer.

"Hey bloke, can I buy you a drink?" Brian heard, while walking home from work near the wharf. He recognized the guy as a runner for new immigrants arriving but had never met him before. It had been a long, exhausting day, so he accepted. After all, it was hard to turn down a drink with a fellow Irishman! "How are you and your family getting along?"

"It has been a struggle, but we are getting by all right. Workdays are long, and wages aren't outstanding, but they pay the bills," Brian replied.

"Well, I may be able to help you out a bit. My employer needs a few more good men. If you are interested, I can connect you with my boss."

"What kind of work are you talking about?"

"Delivery work. You know, moving products from the warehouse to the buyer. Initially, it involves loading and unloading for deliveries, but if you do well, you can work up to being a driver."

"What kind of... product?" Brian asked hesitantly. "And what does it pay?"

"Oh, a variety of products. My boss can explain it all to you if you are interested. I can tell you this, the pay is much better than what you are getting now! I can set up a meeting with my boss for tomorrow if you would like."

"I guess it can't hurt to listen."

"OK, be at the O'Kelly Pub at noon tomorrow."

The meeting went well, and the offer was very generous. The only catch...Brian would be loading bootlegged alcohol to be delivered to local speakeasies. Brian recognized there would be a level of risk, but these were desperate times. If he was ever going to get his family out of NYC, this could provide the means. He wouldn't tell Elizabeth what he would be loading, only that he has a new job loading for delivery and will be making much better money. She would be pleased.

Two months into his job, Brian felt good about his

increase in income and the prospects of getting his family out of Manhattan. The living conditions had been deplorable, and Elizabeth had to work odd jobs to help out. His daughter Michelle, now 18, had also been working by cleaning a couple of local businesses after hours. Life had been difficult, but the McCarthys have stayed together. They frequently talked about leaving NYC and moving west to Butte, to the mines where Marcus Daly had told them of opportunity and a better life. With Brian's new job, he had been able to put away a small sum of money. A few months more, and it would be enough to get them across the country and out of this dangerous city.

"Elizabeth, we have reason to celebrate," Brian said excitedly one evening after working all day.

"Celebrate? What do we have to celebrate?" she asked.

"You are looking at a man who just got a promotion," he said. " I am soon to be the lead driver and have a couple of guys working under me. My boss says I have been doing a great job and offered to increase my pay and responsibilities. Now get your coat, we are going to celebrate."

"Where are we going?" Elizabeth asked cautiously.

"To Club 596. My boss is taking us to dinner and drinks."

Two hours later, they had finished dinner and were enjoying drinks. Tom Sullivan, Brian's boss, had been very generous with both dinner and compliments regarding Brian's work.

"Let me give you a ride home, it's freezing tonight, " Sullivan said. They were just a few blocks from home, but Brian felt obliged to accept the ride and didn't want Elizabeth to have to walk in the cold.

"Thank you, Mr. Sullivan, we would appreciate the ride," said Brian.

Elizabeth added, "Yes, thank you, Mr. Sullivan. Not just for dinner but for providing my husband this opportunity. It will make a great difference for our family."

"I told you, call me Tom. No need for formality. We are friends now."

They stepped out into the cold evening. Brian couldn't help but smile, as he thought about the good fortune he has had the past few months. It was one thing to land a job delivering but now he was getting a promotion as well. Looking at Elizabeth in her long coat and scarf around her neck to keep her warm, he thought of the difficulties they have had to endure. The long trip across the Atlantic, loss of their son, miserable living conditions near the wharf, and all the hard work. For the first time in a long time, Brian was optimistic. He could sense that their life was changing for the better. Their dream of going west to Montana was attainable. It was just a matter of time now. He just needed a few more months to save enough to make their dream a reality.

Just as they approached Mr. Sullivan's car, the roar of another vehicle pulling alongside drew their attention. Traffic was always busy in New York City, but this car approached very quickly and suddenly came to a stop. Rolling down the window, the passenger yelled, "Hey Sullivan, we told you to stay out of our territory." Then he opened fire with a machine gun. Sullivan fell to the ground with a bullet to his forehead.

Brian grabbed Elizabeth and pulled her toward cover. Brian locked eyes with the shooter, but before he could react, both he and Elizabeth were shot from short range. Clearly, the gunman wanted no witnesses. The mob had struck again.

Michelle was devastated by the news. Life had been challenging since they left Ireland. They left because of poverty, the lack of opportunity for the promise of jobs, and a new life in America. Marcus Daly had told them about the opportunities in the mines in Butte. For over a year, they had been working and saving what they could to travel to Butte to start a new life. Now, suddenly and tragically, she was all alone. She had already lost her brother on the trip across the Atlantic and now both parents. Sure, she had a couple of cousins in NYC and some friends but nothing to keep her. Searching through her father's belongings at the apartment, she found the money her father had put away. She recognized that the time had come to get out of New York City, to fulfill the dream of her family. But now she must do it alone.

Chapter 13

Butte, Montana

The Belmont Bar, on the corner of Mercury and Arizona streets, was just a block from the Empire Hotel. It was a good location, but not great. The primary business street was Main Street, which was a few blocks away. The busiest part of Main Street was well north of the Belmont, and it had several bars along its way. The Belmont was considered to be in a secondary business area. After all, it was just a block from the Empire, Pleasant Alley, and the cribs. It certainly attracted a fair amount of traffic, particularly the men of Butte.

Theresa and Nick considered the Belmont to be a reasonable risk. Although they had some money saved, it was not nearly enough for a full down payment to buy the bar. Neither of them was considered a reasonable risk by banks, so they needed to find alternative financing. And Butte had a fair number of those willing to help finance but usually at a significant price. One such person was Milo Ivankovich, owner of the Empire Hotel. He had many dealings throughout Butte and connections to facilitate financing for almost any type of business.

"So, you want to buy a bar, do you?" Ivankovich asked.

"Yes, we are eager to move forward and are confident we can make it work. We just need a little help," replied

Nick.

"How much help do you need?"

"Well, we have about half of the down payment. If you could help us out with the remainder, we would be very appreciative."

"Now, why would I want to take a risk with the likes of you two? Have you ever operated a bar before?"

"No," Theresa interjected. "But we have certainly spent plenty of time around bars, and I have worked in bars for several years. The Belmont has a good track record, and we see no reason it won't continue."

"Do you have any collateral?" Milo asked.

"No. If we did, we would be at the bank right now," Theresa responded.

"I see. Well, I can loan you the money, but it will cost you. I will give you six months to show me you can operate it successfully and pay me back. If you don't pay me back at the end of six months, there will be serious consequences, including me taking over the bar. I expect regular payments and no excuses. My men will be keeping an eye on both of you. Any failure to comply with our agreement will be dealt with swiftly and firmly. Do you understand?"

Nick looked at Theresa, and they cautiously nodded.

"I will have an agreement put together. But make no mistake, failure to meet the terms of our agreement will not be tolerated." With that, he nodded to the door, making clear that the conversation was over.

Theresa and Nick were as excited as they could be. The opportunity they had been looking for was right in front of them; A chance to make a good living, be their own bosses and work together. They understood that they would be taking some chances, but what worthwhile business opportunity didn't have risks? They were both very hard workers and motivated to make it work. What could possibly go wrong?

Chapter 14

Train from NYC to Chicago

The train trip across the country from New York City to Butte was slow, giving Michelle plenty of time to devise her plan. The promise of opportunity in the Butte mines was foremost in her thinking. The McCarthy family dream to leave Ireland and make it in the mines in Butte started well over a year ago. Now Michelle's parents were dead, as were the chances of her family benefitting from the opportunities of working in the mines. Or so it seemed.

But there must be a way, she thought. Michelle was not yet ready to give up on the family dream. She was tall and muscular at 5"9", 165 pounds. She was also somewhat masculine looking with petite breasts and narrow, almost shapeless hips. Her skin was fair and lightly freckled. She had light red hair with very light eyebrows. She had always considered herself to be reasonably strong and was accustomed to hard work, having held several manual jobs to help her family.

A plan began to develop in her mind. What if... could she...would she be able to pull it off? Her voice certainly wasn't deep but wouldn't be considered feminine necessarily. There were many young men with voices similar in tone and pitch to hers. And it wasn't unusual to see Irish men with little to no facial hair well into adulthood.

In addition, no one knew her in Butte. She was well aware that there were plenty of Irish immigrants living in Butte. She could likely blend in with them pretty quickly and easily. A man's hairstyle, tight elastic wrap around her chest, and a few minor changes in mannerisms, and her plan might just work. It would be risky, but so was the life of a single woman trying to make it in a man's world, especially in a rough and tough, blue-collar town like Butte, Montana.

As the train arrived in Chicago, Michelle decided the time had arrived to give her developing plan a trial run. She had a full day layover before moving on. First, Michelle did some clothes shopping – an inexpensive men's outfit. She chose light gray trousers with an extra-wide waistband (Hollywood trousers) with no belt loops, which had become popular by young men in the 1930s, then purchased a sweater vest to match, a white dress shirt, and a tie to complement. Michelle told the salesman that she was buying them as a gift for her recently married husband, explaining that they were nearly the same size. She then purchased a pair of essential oxford shoes and socks.

Next, she went to her hotel room and started working on her hair. She cut it short enough to look like a man's length but purposefully kept it a little long and shaggy. She then put on her new clothes and headed to a local barber. She asked him to give her a Clark Gable hairstyle, which had become popular recently.

Going back to her room, she decided it was time to test out her plan. "Mickey McCarthy" entered the coffee shop and sat near a window. As the waitress approached, Mickey tensed as she rehearsed her line in her mind.

"Good afternoon, sir," the waitress said. "What can I get you today?"

Mickey looked up, cleared her throat, and in a voice, a little deeper than intended, replied, "Just coffee, black, and a slice of apple pie." She watched closely as the waitress took her order, looking for any sign that she thought something was odd or unusual.

After what seemed like several minutes, the waitress casually said, "Yes, sir. It will be just a minute."

Mickey took a deep breath and exhaled. So far, so good!

Before boarding the train the next morning, Mickey purchased some more casual clothing for her trip west. She was able to sell most of her women's clothing items at a nearby thrift store. If Mickey was going to make this work, she needed to go completely in. No trace of her past as a woman could be apparent to anyone she met – onward to Butte and her new life with a small degree of confidence that her plan would work. But also, a bit of anxiety about the uncertainty of what lies ahead.

Chapter 15

Butte, Montana

The first three months at the Belmont Bar had gone well. Business wasn't exactly booming, but they had been able to pay their bills, including payroll, with a little extra. They made an additional payment to Ivankovich, and they were hoping that in three more months, they would have enough to pay off the remainder to rid themselves of the obligation. A couple of weeks into the fourth month, Nick told Theresa that they didn't have enough to cover payroll. She didn't understand. It seemed that business was going pretty well, and she hadn't noticed any significant changes from the previous months.

"We are going to have to tighten our belts," Nick told her. "No needless purchases, and you and I are going to have to work longer hours. We will have to let Michael go, and we need to generate more business somehow."

"I can hardly keep going now. We have no time for anything else. We spend every waking hour at the bar as it is," Theresa said in frustration. It didn't make sense to her that there wasn't enough money to cover the bills and payroll.

"Don't worry, I will come up with a solution. Just give it a few more weeks. I am sure we can get things back on track." Nick responded.

The next month was busy at the bar. They had been

working long hours without any days off and cut expenses as much as possible. Theresa was pleased with how hard they had worked and the positive changes they had made. She was confident that they would be able to pay the bills and have a little extra to put away.

At the end of the month, Nick announced, "Well, we can pay our bills but not much else."

"How can that be?" Theresa asked. "We have been working our tails off, and business has been good."

"Yes, and we need to keep it up for a few more months. I know it is hard, but if we are going to make this work, we have to keep pushing. After a couple of more months, I promise that we will be able to slow down and hire some help again."

The frustration was building, as was the stress in their marriage. Theresa was in near disbelief. Surely they had done better than the previous month, hadn't they? If they didn't turn a profit this month, then she didn't know how they could. Their dream of owning their own bar was beginning to slip away. If they were going to save their vision, they would have to do something desperate.

Nick tried to assure Theresa that things would be okay. He had a plan but was not about to tell Theresa. He was sure his plan would begin to pay off soon. If not, they would be in serious trouble, and he was not about to let that happen.

Chapter 16

Arrival in Butte

Mickey was not sure what to expect as she approached Butte but was surprised at what she saw. Having passed over the Continental Divide, the bus descended into Butte from the east. Looking northwest, it was easy for her to understand why they named the city Butte. Projecting up from the flat terrain to the south was a perfectly formed butte. Dotting the hillside were multiple headframes marking the entrance to the hundreds of underground mines. The density of the population on the "butte" was surprising as well. Neighborhoods were intermixed with mining headframes and shafts throughout the hill though she didn't realize the ethnic diversity of the communities.

Stepping off the bus that she boarded in Billings, she took in the view around her. The Continental Divide filled the skyline to the east. Looking west, the blue sky filled the space between the Butte Hill and the Pintler mountains toward Anaconda some 25 miles away. To the north, the Butte hill arose from the flat land and the main highway, which she traveled nearly all the way from Chicago, bringing her to Butte. To the south, well beyond her view, was the small rural town of Dillon, Montana, and beyond that the eastern Idaho towns of Idaho Falls and Pocatello. Both excitement and trepidation filled her as she retrieved her small bags from the luggage compartment. What if her deception was discovered? What if she was unable to find work in the mines after all she has been through? Surely she would be accepted by her fellow Irishmen who inhabit the Dublin Gulch neighborhood. She had heard from others about the Irish of Butte. Indeed, they would welcome her and help her settle, assuming her plan worked as she hoped and prayed that it did.

After asking a few questions at the bus station, she was directed to Maloney's Pub on Main Street. A favorite gathering place for many Irish immigrants, Mickey was optimistic she would find some help getting settled.

"Howya Mick, you look like you are a wee bit lost," the bartender said as Mickey stood at the doorway to the pub. Startled, she greeted the bartender wearily. "Just feeling a little knackered after a long day. I could use a drink". And a little help, she thought to herself.

"I haven't seen you here before," said the bartender.

"I just got into town," she replied. "Looking for a place to stay and hoping to find work at one of the mines."

"Where have you come from?"

She thought about her long journey, the family tragedies, and the challenges ahead of her. But she decided now wasn't the time to share details. Maybe she never would. She simply replied, "Cork County, Ireland originally but looking for a new start."

He directed her to a friend in Dublin Gulch, who had a boarding house. "She will be able to get you set up for a while and help you get lined up with someone to talk with about a job." With mining booming and turnover frequent because of the difficult work, she should have no trouble finding a job. So far, so good. Her plan was working out perfectly with no one appearing the least bit suspicious.

Chapter 17

Butte

Desperate times call for drastic measures, someone once said. And Nick was undoubtedly feeling the desperation. If his plan didn't bear some fruit soon, they would lose the chance to purchase the bar and maybe more. He was so confident that he could generate significant cash quickly but hadn't really considered what would happen if he didn't. He had always been pretty successful before, felt he had a knack for it, yet he also knew there were no guarantees. It was still a risk, but one he thought was worth taking. After all, when he was successful, their dreams would be realized, and they would be proud owners of the Belmont Bar.

But of course, there were inherent risks in every type of get-rich quick scheme. And this scheme was not an exception. The cards don't always fall your way. He had frequently played in the back room of the Metals Bar and did pretty well for the most part. Sure, he had the occasional losses, but he seemed to win more than he lost. At first, he played with small amounts of his money, but over the past several weeks, he played with more and more money. And not just his money but the Belmont's money. Early success got him thinking that he could use some of the bar's money to generate quick cash that would allow them to pay off the loan sooner. He began rationalizing that with his early success, it was the right thing, the wise thing to do. Of course, he kept it from Theresa. No sense in letting her know until the time was right – when he could produce enough money for the rest of the down payment. To surprise her, to impress her, to fulfill her dream.

The Tuesday night poker game started out well for Nick. He was hot, winning three of the first five hands. Feeling confident, maybe even cocky, he gambled with more significant amounts than he had before. He sensed that this was his night. He was going to win enough to make that down payment they had been working so hard for.

Holding three kings in his hand, Nick discarded the other two. He had already placed a substantial bet, having been on a winning streak the past few hands. Two other players folded, leaving just Nick and one other gentleman in the game. As the other two cards were dealt, he could hardly contain himself inside. A pair of tens! Remaining as calm as he possibly could, Nick increased his bet with the remainder of his money. The gentlemen across from him eyed him carefully, looking for any sign that he might be bluffing. But Nick remained stoic, showing no outward signs that might tip off his opponent. Nick was confident that he had a winning hand but was hopeful his opponent thought he was bluffing and matched his bet. Doing so, the man called. A broad smile crossed Nick's face, as he laid down his hand. Three kings and two tens for a full house. Slowly his opponent revealed his hand – four ladies! Nick's heart sank in disbelief. Not only had he lost the game and nearly all of their money, but he had effectively lost the Belmont Bar. Now they didn't have the money to pay their bills, let alone money for the payment to Ivankovich.

Chapter 18

Butte

Cabby Young's familiarity with Milo Ivankovich went back several years. After a few years of bouncing from one low-paying job to another as a cook, Young was eager to find a way to make some additional money. And Ivankovich, for his part, needed people to enforce the many ventures he had around Butte. His dealings with the underbelly of Butte frequently brought him into relationships with some unsavory characters. This required unconventional means of enforcing his transactions much of the time. He needed people who were willing to bypass the law when necessary to make sure agreements were honored. People who were not averse to using violence, or at least the threat of violence, to get the job done.

Cabby was such a person. He had lived his entire life in Butte and spent much time on the streets. He saw and experienced the best and worst of Butte. Growing up, he had participated in the ethnic clashes that were frequent in the Butte neighborhoods. He had been involved in many fights around Butte. Most were fistfights among the neighborhood gangs, but they became much more violent and bloody on occasion. Weapons of various kinds were employed, usually sticks or metal bars, but occasionally knives and other deadly weapons had been used. Cabby had never personally killed anyone but had witnessed killings on a few occasions. He was not opposed to using deadly force if the situation required it but preferred other means to resolve conflict or enforce deals.

Ivankovich was well aware of Young and his reputation. He had both casual and first-hand experience with him over the years. Young had a reputation that Ivankovich knew was well deserved. Anyone who tangled with Young was in for a battle, and nearly everyone in town knew it. He was just the person Ivankovich needed as an enforcer.

"Hey, Young, you got a minute?" he asked him as he walked outside the Empire.

"Depends, what's it about?"

"I've got a proposition I think you might be interested in."

"What makes you think I would be interested?"

"For starters, it pays well, very well, if done well."

"I've got a job already," replied Young.

"You mean that cook job? That's peanuts compared to what you can make working for me. Besides, you can continue your job and help me on the side. I can promise you it will be worth your time."

"How dangerous will it be?"

"If you want to make more money, you're going to have to take some risk. But I will make sure you are compensated for the risk. You will have to threaten occasionally and maybe even use a little force when necessary."

"I can handle that without a problem. It just depends

on what kind of money you are talking about."

An hour later, they had a business agreement. Cabby Young was a new enforcer for Milo Ivankovich's enterprises. He was now on retainer to help make sure Ivankovich's many business agreements were carried out as agreed upon.

Chapter 19

Several weeks had gone by since Mickey started working in the Anselmo Mine, a mine that began in 1887. The work was dirty and physically demanding, but after the first week of being stiff and sore, Mickey found she could handle it pretty well. In fact, Mickey rather liked it and was proud that she was able to handle it physically. Initially, she was afraid that she would not be able to keep up with the men, but she had been able to hold her own. More importantly, no one had suspected anything. Her plan was working out just fine. The money she was able to make in the mine was much more than she would have made in the service jobs she likely would have had to take. Living in a small boarding room in Dublin Gulch with the other Irish immigrants proved to be great. Here she felt a connection with her homeland, a sense of community, and safety in a new place. She had made several friends but was very careful not to get too close for fear of exposing her deception. If anyone were to find out, it would be disastrous, certainly losing her job but likely much more.

She often went to the bars after work to unwind. Not a big drinker anyway, she was careful not to become inebriated. She did not want to foolishly say or do something that might give herself away. After trying several bars nearby, she found herself drawn to the Belmont. It was just large enough to attract a safe crowd and on weekend nights, offering live music and a small area for those wishing to play cards. She was not one to gamble, but she did enjoy watching on occasion. It amazed her that hardworking men would risk losing money that they had worked so hard for. She understood that the lure of making quick money was what drove many of them to the tables. But for her, it just wasn't worth the risk.

This particular Friday night, the Belmont was hopping. It was payday, and the miners were there to unwind. The card room was busy with both tables full and several standing nearby waiting for their turn to try their luck. A gentleman played a variety of tunes on the piano, and couples were dancing on the small dance floor. It was standing room only at the bar, and the bartender was having difficulty keeping up with everyone. No one seemed to mind since everyone was having a great time.

Theresa and Nick were doing all they could to keep up. They could use more help, and they hadn't expected quite this many. It was always a guess how busy it would be on any given night, but since the bar hadn't been making a lot of profit, they were trying to keep overhead to a minimum. Neither of them remembered that it was payday at the mines, so now they were paying the price for not having extra help.

After having a few beers, Mickey needed to use the restroom. She had been talking with a friend and waited a little longer than she should have but finally excused herself. Mickey worked her way through the bar to the restroom and found the men's room was full, with a few others waiting their turn. She didn't dare use the women's but couldn't wait any longer. Exiting out the back door, Mickey went behind a garbage dumpster where others taking a leak couldn't see her. Just as she squatted down to pee, Nick came out the door with a trash bag. They locked eyes, and Mickey could see it in his eyes. She knew instantly she was caught in her deceit. Panic quickly hit her. How could she have been so careless?

Nick turned and returned to the bar. Mickey was quick to follow but didn't know what to say or do. She couldn't allow Nick to expose her to others. Her job, her new way of life, maybe even her life itself depended on keeping her secret from others.

"Nick, please, I need to talk to you."

"I can't. I am too busy," Nick said, trying to avoid her.

"I beg you," Mickey replied in desperation. "Can we meet in the morning then? I need to explain."

Nick thought for a minute. I guess there would be no harm in hearing her out. "Okay," he said reluctantly. "Come by the bar around ten."

"Thank you. But please don't tell anyone about this. At least until you hear me out."

Nick couldn't imagine what Mickey could tell him to explain what he clearly saw. This man, or so everyone believed, was clearly not who she claimed to be. But why? It didn't make sense. What was going on? And did he really want to know? He wished he had not seen anything. But he can't change that now.

Mickey, for her part, tossed and turned all night. What was she going to do? Things had been going so well with an excellent job with good pay. She made friends and enjoyed living in Dublin Gulch. Everything had been going great until she made an unfortunate and careless decision. She was confident she was all alone and hidden from view. Having a few drinks made her let her guard down. Now she had to figure out a way to rectify the situation. Surely Nick was a reasonable man and would understand. After all, he could see the difficulty of a woman making it in a man's world. Yes, after explaining it to him, Nick would understand. But...what if he didn't?

Nick was busy cleaning up the bar when Mickey arrived. Looking up, their eyes met again, just like the night before. But this time, Nick saw not a fearful look, but rather a pleading look in Mickey's eyes.

"I need to explain," Mickey began. She told him the whole story from leaving Ireland with her family to the tragedies they experienced in New York City, to the plans they had to come to Butte. She explained her father's dream to go to Butte and work in the mines after hearing Marcus Daly's promises of opportunity.

"I was desperate. I didn't want to stay in New York City, and I knew that a single woman coming to Butte was risky. I didn't feel I could make it on my own working service jobs, so working in the mines was my best option. I was sure I could handle the work, and it would fulfill my family's dream. The plan just came together as I thought about it. And for several months, the plan was working perfectly."

"Until last night," Nick said.

"Yes, until last night when I was careless. But it doesn't have to end. Surely you can understand. There must be something I can do to convince you to keep this quiet."

Nick considered Mickey's situation for a few minutes. Why should he keep it quiet, and what would it benefit him? But what good would it do to tell others? He liked Mickey well enough, and to keep a secret like this would not be very hard. But then again, maybe there could be a benefit to keeping the secret. He still had not told Theresa about the money he lost gambling. He was hoping something would happen to get some of the money back. Maybe this was his opportunity.

"I don't know," Nick replied. "You are asking a lot of me. I am not sure I can keep it, and even if I could, what good would it be to me?"

A sense of panic rose up in Mickey. Her life would be ruined if this got out. What would Nick have to gain by exposing her? Mickey didn't know but couldn't take a chance. "Maybe we could come to an understanding, an agreement of sorts."

"I am listening," Nick replied.

"How are things going at the bar?" Mickey asked. "I hear you and Theresa are trying to buy the place."

"That is the plan. Once we come up with a little more money for the remainder of the down payment. It has been going a little slower than we expected, but I am confident we will get there."

"Well, maybe I can help. I have been able to put away a little extra. In exchange for your silence, I would be willing to help you out."

Nick was intrigued. This was not something he expected. Maybe this was the opportunity they needed. And how could he turn it down? It was an opportunity to recover some of his losses and fulfill their dream of owning the bar. And he would only have to pledge his silence in exchange. It seemed too good to turn down.

"How much are you short?" Mickey asked.

"A grand."

"I can get you $300 now and another $300 by the end of the year."

Nick considered it for a couple of minutes. Theresa would be so excited. But would he even need to tell her right now? After all, she would ask questions, and it would be hard to explain where the money came from without exposing the source. No, it was best to keep it to himself for now. "You have a deal. I will keep it to myself in exchange for $300 now and another $300 at the end of the year. I give you my word."

Chapter 20

As the end of the month approached, Theresa knew having enough money to pay Ivankovich and the bar's bills was going to be close. The first part of the month had been a little bit slow, but this week had been much busier. But then it always was around payday. She was pretty sure they would have enough to cover month-end expenses, but she was hoping for a bit extra to go toward paying off Ivankovich. The sooner they could get out from under that loan, the better.

"Nick, how are we doing with finances this month?

He smiled to himself. "Oh, I think we are going to be just fine. It has been a good couple of weeks, so we should get all the bills paid and maybe even have a little leftover."

He had no intention of telling her about the money from Mickey, which he had tucked away in a secret place in the closet of their apartment, or about the money he had lost gambling. She would find out soon enough, but he thought it best to keep it to himself.

"I would sure like to get Ivankovich paid off," she said. "I hate having to owe that man anything. I don't trust him and don't want to deal with him any longer than we have to."

"Don't you worry about it. I am sure that by the end of the year, we will be able to get Ivankovich paid off, and the Belmont will be ours. There is no reason to think business will slow down now, and if we keep working hard, the money will be there."

"I don't know, Nick. Things are just so unpredictable. One week we are so busy we can hardly keep up, and the next, we barely make enough to cover the day's payroll."

"That is just the nature of the business," he replied. "Over time, things will balance out, and we will pay off Ivankovich and no longer have to worry about him."

Theresa wasn't so confident. Nick took care of the money and books, but she sensed that things were not going as well as he indicated. He had been paying the bills, and any extra at the end of the month, he put in a safe deposit box in the office at the bar for paying off the loan to Ivankovich. She had watched him put money there several times and was hoping there was enough to get the loan paid off at the end of the year. She was trusting him that things would work out.

Nearly three more months had gone by, and the bar had been steadily getting busier. The clientele had been more consistent, and Theresa was feeling much better about the progress toward paying off the loan. It was now December, and everyone was getting excited about the holidays. Patrons had been in the holiday spirit and quite generous with tipping at the bar. Theresa was as confident as she could be that the Belmont will soon be theirs.

Chapter 21

It can be bitterly cold in Butte in the winter. At nearly a mile in elevation, the temperature frequently can dip below zero, and the wind chill makes being outside almost unbearable. That December was particularly brutal. Already nearly 4.5 ft. of snow had fallen, and it was snowing heavily now. The wind was blowing in from the west, and the snow was drifting on the roadways. Driving up Main or Montana Streets to the business district was nearly impossible, even with road crews working diligently to remove the snow. The plowed snow piles had reached ten feet in places. That night, almost no one was out. The bar was empty except for Theresa and Mr. Sullivan, who lived just around the corner from the bar. Nick had left several hours ago, and Theresa expected him back soon.

Suddenly, the bar door opened, and a bitterly cold wind entered. The force of the wind was strong, and the door slammed shut almost as quickly as it opened. Theresa turned in time to see Milo Ivankovich shaking the snow off his boots and rubbing his hands together in a futile effort to warm them. Theresa detested the man, and it was all she could do to greet him with a smile.

"Where's your husband?" he demanded.

"He is not here, why? Theresa responded.

"I want my money, and I want it today."

"Our payment is not due for 2 weeks. You will get it then as promised and on schedule," Theresa replied.

"On schedule? I haven't received a payment for over three months. And I am tired of playing games with you two. He promised he would have it to me by this week, and I have not seen or heard from either of you. Where is that bastard?"

"What are you talking about? I saw him put money into the safe deposit box at the end of every month. That money was set aside for the payment to you. "

"I don't know what he did with that money, but it didn't come to me. And I have run out of patience. You tell that husband of yours that he better have my money by the end of the week, or there will be hell to pay." With that, Ivankovich stormed out of the bar.

What is going on, Theresa thought to herself. She watched Nick put that money aside, and he had told her he was making payments on the loan. There must be a mistake – a misunderstanding.

She quickly went to the office and found a safe deposit box. It was empty. Theresa was overwhelmed with anxiety and dread. No, there must be an explanation. Surely it would make sense when Nick got back. He must have put the money somewhere else for safekeeping. He wouldn't put the bar and their future at risk.

Chapter 22

Nick was in full panic. Just as he turned the corner, he saw Ivankovich leaving the bar. He had the money from Mickey, both the original $300 and $300 more that she gave him yesterday as promised. But it was not nearly enough. The money he lost gambling was too much to recover. He could use the cash from Mickey to pay Ivankovich, but there wouldn't be enough to cover the month's bills. If he used it to pay the bills, then he couldn't pay Ivankovich, who would be furious. It appeared as though he was already looking for him. He was now three months behind, and Ivankovich was not known to be a patient man. He had to come up with a plan, quick, or he would be in serious trouble. Nick hurried back to his car. He needed to get away from Ivankovich and from Theresa until he could come up with a plan.

Backed into a corner, he reasoned his only option now was to take the money he received from Mickey and run. Theresa didn't know about Mickey's money and likely thought that Nick had taken the money from the bar and deposited it in the bank. Before she realized that he had not, he would be long gone.

Nick returned to their apartment and rapidly gathered up some of his belongings. He recognized that he probably didn't have much time before Theresa would be looking for him to get some answers. More importantly, Ivankovich would have his men searching for him and applying whatever pressure necessary to get his money. Nick hurriedly put some clothes into a suitcase, scoured the house looking for any money that Theresa may have hidden away, and went to the service station to gas up for his exit from town.

Milo Ivankovich was furious. He knew he shouldn't have trusted Nick Evans. He and Theresa were a big risk and Ivankovich should have kept a closer eye on them.

"Petrovich, this is Ivankovich. I want you to grab one of your men and go find Nick Evans. Under no circumstances is he to be allowed to leave Butte. Do whatever is necessary to find him and bring him to me."

"Are you talking about the guy running the Belmont Bar?"

"That's the guy. He owes me some money and I have reason to believe he is about to run. His wife, Theresa, is at the bar and claims she doesn't know where he went. I tend to believe her but just in case, check out their apartment and the bar in case he returned. Get right on it, I have a feeling we don't have much time."

As Nick was fueling his car at the Texaco on Montana Street, he nervously watched his surroundings. He knew Ivankovich was angry and was sure he would have his guys on the lookout for him by now. Just as he got back into his car, Nick noticed a vehicle driving unusually slow up Montana. The car didn't look familiar, but he recognized the driver as one of Ivankovich's men. Quickly, he lowered himself in the front seat so that he wouldn't be seen. He wasn't sure if the men knew what kind of car he was driving but he didn't want to take any chances. The car turned right onto Galena Street toward the Empire Hotel. Nick started his car and headed south on Montana toward the highway leading out of town toward Helena.

Petrovich and his partner were watching closely for any sign of Nick. They checked around the Empire and the Belmont but when they saw no sign of him, they doubled back and returned to Montana Street. As they reached Montana, Petrovich noticed a Ford accelerating south toward the highway and began to follow. Ivankovich told him that Nick Evans drove an older model Ford Coupe, but the men hadn't gotten a good look of the driver. Glancing in his rearview mirror, Nick noticed a car following several blocks behind and picking up speed. It didn't appear as though they had noticed Nick when they drove by the gas station, but he couldn't be certain. He calmly turned east on Front Street, made a quick right turn onto a side street and then backed into the alley behind a tree so that he was partially hidden from view. From there he still had a clear view of Front Street and watched carefully to see if they followed. A few minutes later the other car turned onto Front Street as well. Ivankovich's men drove slowly down Front and it was now clear they were looking for Nick. After they passed, Nick waited a few minutes, slowly backed out of the alley in the opposite direction, wound through the neighborhood taking several side streets, and eventually reached the highway at its east end. Before pulling onto the highway he parked behind a delivery truck and waited several minutes to make sure Ivankovich's men had not seen him. Once he was sure he had lost them, Nick accelerated on the highway toward Helena. There was no sign of the car that he suspected was searching for him, so he was finally able to calm his breathing and begin planning the next steps.

Chapter 23

A week later, Jack Duggan went to the Belmont to talk with Theresa. She had reported that Nick had disappeared without a trace, and their money was nowhere to be found. She had checked with every bank in town, and there was no record of any deposits made by Nick Evans on behalf of the Belmont Bar or himself. Theresa had searched all over Butte, and there had been no sign of Nick. No one had seen or heard from him in over a week now. She had no choice but to turn to the police for help.

"When was the last time you saw your husband, Mrs. Evans?" asked Duggan.

"It was eight days ago now. He left to run an errand and didn't return."

"Where was he going?"

"He didn't say, but I assumed he was going to pay bills."

"What kind of bills?

"Bills we owed from expenses at the bar."

"Can you be more specific?"

"The usual bills from running a bar. Liquor store, bar supplies, that kind of thing."

"Do you have any outstanding loans?'

Reluctantly, Theresa told him about the loan from Ivankovich for the down payment. She said to him that Ivankovich had come to the bar last week and said that they were behind by more than three months and that

Ivankovich was furious. He was looking for Nick. "I had no idea he had not been making payments," Theresa said.

"What did Ivankovich say? Did he make any threats?"

"As he was leaving the bar, he said that Nick better have the money to him by the end of the week or there would be hell to pay."

"And did you tell Nick what Ivankovich said?"

"No. I haven't seen Nick since before Ivankovich was at the bar."

Chapter 24

"What the hell do you mean, you can't find him?" Ivankovich screamed at Petrovich.

"We searched everywhere boss. He disappeared." Replied Petrovich.

"Clearly you didn't search everywhere, or you would have found him. Get back out there and look again and don't come back until you find him."

That two-bit hustler Evans had stiffed him and was now nowhere to be found. Sure, in the broad scope of things, the dollar amount was not huge, but it was the principle. No one was going to get away with not paying their debts to Milo Ivankovich. He was sure that Theresa Evans had nothing to do with default, but there was no way he would let her continue operating the bar without making the loan payments. As for Nick Evans, Ivankovich swore he would eventually find him, and a severe price would be paid. He would find someone to take over the bar to keep it operational, and Theresa would be removed. The small apartment above the bar where they had been living since they began operating the bar would need to be vacated. But Ivankovich wasn't totally heartless. After all, Theresa was a victim in this as well. The least he could do was provide her a room at the Empire until she could get on her feet again.

As for Nick, that was a totally different story. It was time to call another one of his enforcers since Petrovich had failed miserably – time to put Cabby Young to work.

"Young, I've got a job for you," Ivankovich said.

"What kind of job?"

"You know a guy by the name of Nick Evans?"

"The guy who has been running the Belmont?"

"That's him. I need you to find him and bring him to me. He owes me some money and has decided he doesn't need to pay me. Turns out he disappeared about 10 days ago, and nobody seems to know what happened to him. That includes his wife, Theresa. She claims she doesn't know where he is and hasn't heard from him since he disappeared."

"Any ideas where he has gone?" asked Young.

"No idea. That's why I need you. I want you to find out if Evans is still in Butte or if he has skipped town. And if he has, where."

Cabby considered going directly to Theresa Evans to talk with her but decided that might not be wise at this point. He thought it possible that Theresa knew where Nick Evans had gone. If he talked directly with Theresa, she might tip off Nick that Cabby was searching for him and then he would really disappear. No, it was better, at least for now, that Theresa Evans didn't know Cabby was looking for her husband. Cabby stood to make some very good money if he found Nick Evans and he didn't want to blow it. He decided he must be patient and calculate his moves very carefully.

Chapter 25

Mickey heard on the street that Nick Evans had disappeared. She had not seen or heard from him since she made a second payment a little more than a month before. As far as she knew, he was the only one that knew her secret, but she couldn't be sure he hadn't told anyone, particularly his wife, Theresa. Or that he wouldn't be back to blackmail her for more money. She had stayed away from the Belmont since their agreement several months back. She reasoned that if Nick told his wife, she would have confronted her by now. But now that Evans had disappeared, she wasn't sure what to think. What if he told his wife? If he did tell her, then she may expose Mickey. Or maybe she would try to blackmail her. Mickey decided she needed to be alert and keep an eye on Theresa while watching for any sign of Nick.

Later that afternoon, as Mickey exited the First National Bank on North Montana Street, she was startled by a voice coming from just outside the main door.

"Hello, Mickey, you got a minute?" asked the familiar voice.

"I... I guess so," she said to Theresa as she turned toward her. She certainly wasn't expecting to see her and was hoping that they wouldn't come across each other.

"What can I do for you?"

"You can start by explaining what you were discussing with Nick when I saw you outside the bar."

"I don't know what you mean," replied Mickey.

"Don't lie to me. I know your secret." Theresa suspected that Mickey had loaned Nick some money. But Mickey immediately thought that Theresa was referring to her other secret. Her BIG secret. The one she has been hiding since she arrived in Butte. If revealed, the secret would undoubtedly put an end to her job and likely her entire life in Butte.

"I don't know what you are talking about," she said in feigned ignorance.

"I saw you talking with Nick, and he has been acting a bit strange since. Now he has disappeared, and I have no idea where he has gone. I know that it has to do with your conversation. I know what you are up to."

Mickey was a bit confused. Did Theresa know about her secret life? Or was there something else going on? If she did know, why wasn't she just telling her so? And if Nick didn't tell her about her secret life, what was it that she thought she knew? Afraid to push it further, Mickey continued to act as though she didn't know what Theresa was talking about.

"Fine. If you are not going to own up to it, I will have to take it upon myself to take care of things," said Theresa.

Mickey studied Theresa for a few minutes. If she knew she had been living a double life, what would keep her from going to the police? Maybe Theresa had something else in mind? Perhaps she was playing

Mickey to see how she would react? Or maybe she didn't really know anything? But Mickey couldn't take that chance. She really needed to find out how much Theresa knew before it was too late. What did Theresa mean that she would have to take it upon herself to take care of things? Mickey was going to have to keep a very close eye on Theresa. She had made it too far to let it fall apart now.

Theresa was convinced that something was going on between Mickey and Nick. They were very secretive when she saw them talking several weeks ago. Clearly, it was urgent, and when the conversation ended, Nick seemed quite pleased. But Mickey walked away looking very concerned. They had some kind of an agreement, a deal, she was sure of that. But what and why had Nick suddenly disappeared?

A couple of days later, Mickey was driving down Galena Street and made the turn onto Wyoming in front of the Empire. Standing outside the hotel, Theresa was talking with Detective Duggan. Now Mickey was really concerned. What were they discussing? Was she just being paranoid? Or was Theresa sharing the secret Mickey was afraid that Nick shared with her? No, she was just paranoid, she decided. They were likely discussing Nick's disappearance. But Mickey couldn't be sure. She needed to find out what Theresa knew and find out soon.

Chapter 26

Anaconda

Mary and Jeanne hadn't seen or heard from Theresa in several weeks. Mary had heard rumors that Nick had left and that they lost the Belmont. But she sure wasn't going to tell Jeanne. They heard directly from Theresa that they were optimistic about the bar, and certain things were heading in the right direction. With no contact for several weeks now, Mary was afraid the rumors were true.

Jeanne had nearly given up hope that her mother was coming back for them. She had become more and more withdrawn and no longer asked Mary regularly about her mother. With each passing day that she didn't hear from her, she was afraid that her mother wouldn't be back.

Jeanne was now in the seventh grade at St. Peter's School. She had a few friends but was not particularly popular with the rest of the kids. Her lack of parental involvement in her life had shaped her in very complex ways. Sure, she had Mary as an influence in her life, but that was much different than a parent, and the other kids knew that she had no parents involved in her life. She felt different from most of the other kids, most of whom had both parents involved. Jeanne noticed the other kids looked at her differently when she had no parent at school activities or parent-teacher conferences. Jeanne has had to grow up quicker than most kids her age. She took on more responsibilities and had to be much more independent than her peers.

Jeanne stepped off her porch as she headed off to school. Just as she did, a familiar car pulled up. "Momma," she yelled with excitement! Theresa jumped out of the car and hurried over to Jeanne and gave her a big hug.

"I have missed you so much," Jeanne said "I didn't think you were ever going to come back."

"I am sorry I haven't been around, but things have been hectic in Butte."

"Are you here to bring us to Butte with you now? Are we going to live with you and Nick?"

"We can talk about that later," Theresa replied. "You better get on to school now, but we can talk tonight."

Excitedly, Jeanne joined a friend and walked on to school. She wasn't so sure this day would ever come. She had all but lost hope that her mother would come back for them, but now her mother was here to take her with her to Butte to live with her and Nick. She had been hoping and waiting for this day for so long. She would miss living with her grandmother, but being back together with her mother was what she had been hoping and praying for.

"You're back," Mary said cautiously. The kids and I have worried about you. "Why haven't you kept in touch with us these past few months?"

"It's very complicated, mom. That's why I am here. I have some news for you that you probably aren't going to like. But before you say anything, hear me out."

Here we go again, Mary thought to herself but listened as Theresa laid out all that had happened the past several months. She explained the difficulties with the bar, the challenges with paying bills and loan payments. Theresa told her of the disappearance of Nick and the money with him. She shared how they lost the bar and their apartment, that she was now living in a room at the Empire Hotel. She told her that she didn't know where Nick was or if he was coming back.

Tearfully, she acknowledged what Mary already suspected. Theresa was almost penniless and would not be taking the children back with her.

***

Today was a cold and crisp Montana winter day. Typical for this time of year, the sky was bright blue, and feet of white snow had fallen all around town. The temperature was below zero, cold enough that the hair in your nostrils froze, and any exposed skin burned from the cold. But it didn't bother Jeanne a bit. She had been excited all day at school. She couldn't wait to get home to see her mom and make plans for going to Butte to live with her.

Walking up Ash Street, Jeanne turned west on Sixth Street and looked for her mother's car. But it was nowhere in sight. Maybe she parked in the back or was running an errand for gramma, she thought to herself. Approaching the house, she saw the light on in the living room and ran inside excitedly yelling for her mother. But she saw only Mary sitting on the sofa.

"Where is momma?" she asked. "I have so much to tell her and plans to make." But the look on her grandmother's face quickly squashed her excitement.

"I am so sorry, dear," her grandma responded. "Your mother is not here. She went back to Butte. She can't take you with her right now. She wanted to stay to talk with you but said she had to get back to work."

Jeanne burst into tears and ran to her room. How could her mother do this to her...again? She sobbed for several hours and refused to come out of her room. Mary could hardly blame her. Her mother leaving was more heartbreak than any child should have to endure. Jeanne, for her part, resolved never to get her hopes up again. She recognized that her mother didn't want her to live with her, that she would live with her grandmother until she was able to make it on her own. Jeanne further resolved not to rely on anyone but herself. She would do everything she could to make it on her own and trust no one else for her well-being. Jeanne knew it wasn't fair to her grandmother, the one who was always there for her, but also knew that her grandma wouldn't be there forever. She was going to have to depend on no one but herself. She determined right then that she would work hard and be dependent on no one.

Chapter 27

Finding Nick Evans would be a challenge. No one had seen or heard from him in a couple of months. It was near the end of February, and he seemed to have disappeared into thin air. But Cabby Young was determined to find him. After all, there was a strong motivation for him to find Evans. Motivation in the form of a significant payday from Milo Ivankovich. The issue was not that Evans owed Ivankovich a lot of money, but it was the principle. Ivankovich did not tolerate having his loans go unpaid, regardless of the amount. He had a reputation to uphold, which Cabby Young understood, and Ivankovich would make it well worth Young's time to find him.

Young had already done some initial investigation, albeit very confidentially. Checking known hangouts of Evans had yielded nothing. He had asked around, and no one admitted to seeing Evans for weeks or had any idea where he might have gone. Somebody must know his whereabouts, though. It was time for Young to visit Theresa Evans.

Young didn't want her to know he was working for Ivankovich and had been very cautious with his search. He had been careful not to let on that he was working for anyone or why he was interested in Evans. Directly confronting Theresa and asking her questions about

Nick would arouse her suspicions. No, he needed to gain her confidence first and get the information he needed to find him.

Theresa no longer spent much time at the Belmont. It was too painful, a sobering reminder of the dream lost and of Nick, who left her weeks ago with not so much as a note. But of course, she knew why he left – the lack of money. The inability to pay the bills and the loan to Ivankovich was too much for him. She knew that she lost nearly everything – the bar, her husband, and her home. Living in the Empire was not so bad, but indeed not where she wanted to live long term. But for now, it would have to do, at least until she came up with a new plan. She was not sure why she came to the Belmont that day. She hadn't been here for weeks but felt the need to go. Maybe it was just the familiarity. Perhaps it was the hope of seeing old friends, that somehow Nick would be there, and things would be normal again. She knew that would never happen, but something drew her back today.

"Is this seat taken?" she heard a man's voice from behind her.

She had been sitting at the bar lost in thought and was startled for a moment. Without even looking back, she said, "Help yourself."

Cabby Young slid in next to her and smiled. "You look like you could use a friend."

Theresa tried to muster a smile but just couldn't seem to do so.

"Let me buy you a drink," he offered.

Not one to turn down a free drink, especially now that she had little money to her name, she said, "Sure, why not?"

Over the next two hours, Theresa and Cabby shared a few drinks. He was attentive, pleasant, and a good listener. Theresa found herself opening up to him. She had not had anyone to share her frustrations of the past few months, and as she had more to drink, she became less inhibited. It felt good to have someone to share things.

Cabby was careful not to pry too much. He didn't want to expose his motivation to her. There would be time to get information about Nick Evans from her, but he must be patient. For now, he must be satisfied with starting a friendship and progress from there.

"I think I better go home," Theresa finally said. She undoubtedly had a little too much to drink.

Cabby considered offering to take her home but decided against it. Patience, he reminded himself. "I enjoyed our conversation today. Maybe we could do it again sometime?

"I would like that," Theresa responded.

"How about Saturday night? Maybe a few drinks and dancing."

Theresa considered the offer for a couple of minutes. She was still married – at least legally. But she hadn't seen her husband in weeks, didn't know where he was, or if he was ever coming back. What could it hurt? It was only drinks and dancing. She had been pretty lonely, and she genuinely enjoyed his company today.

"I will meet you at Maloney's at eight," she said with a smile, and off she went back to the Empire.

Chapter 28

Mickey was becoming more and more concerned that Nick told Theresa about her secret life. After seeing her talking with Detective Duggan, she was suspicious that she might be getting ready to expose her. After all, Theresa told her that she knew Mickey's secret. But unquestionably, if Theresa had told Duggan, he would have come to talk with Mickey. Maybe Theresa had just been planting a seed with Duggan, just waiting for the most beneficial time to tell him. Perhaps she was planning to blackmail Mickey. Or maybe Theresa didn't know and was talking to Duggan about something unrelated. It was driving her crazy, not knowing for sure what, if anything, Theresa knew. She has got to find out and soon.

Thinking back to that day when she saw Nick and Mickey talking, she recalled the look of anxiety on Mickey's face as they finished talking. It was clear that something was not right and that she was worried. Nick had a confused look like he couldn't quite comprehend something. He looked uncomfortable. Theresa knew that they had met the following morning, though they weren't aware that she saw them. It was also quite clear that after the conversation, Nick looked delighted. The confused look from the night before was gone and replaced by a sense that something good had occurred. But what? And Mickey had seemed relieved. The conversation had been brief, but it appeared that they had reached some kind of agreement and were planning to meet again soon.

Walking west on Galena Street, Theresa gazed west toward Anaconda, where the sun was setting. She thought about Jeanne and wondered how she was getting along with Mary and her brother Raymond. It had to be difficult on them, but Theresa was not ready or able to properly care for them. A tear trailed down her cheek, as she thought about the mess her life had become. Her optimism gone, replaced by a sense that things were falling apart again. She was sure that something odd was going on with Nick and Mickey. It must have to do with money, maybe a loan? But why would he loan Nick money? What did Mickey have to gain? Theresa knew they weren't friends though they did know each other since Mickey regularly frequented the bar. Could Nick have approached Mickey for a loan in desperation? After all, they did not have a lot of options for money. The banks had already turned them down, and they were behind on paying Ivankovich back. He certainly wouldn't go back to Ivankovich for more. The only thing that made sense was that Nick approached Mickey for a loan. But, why Mickey? What would be the motivation to loan Nick money? And why hadn't Nick told Theresa about it? There were just too many unanswered questions.

Walking back toward the Empire, Theresa resolved that she would make changes in her life. She must become more stable in her relationships and committed to caring for her children. Tomorrow Theresa would pay a visit to her children in Anaconda. But first, she had to either find Nick or approach Mickey. She must get answers.

Chapter 29

Escape from Butte

In 1939, six hundred dollars would get you pretty far when you were on the run. But the question was, where to go? The only family Nick had in the United States was his cousin Boris and his wife Theresa, both in Butte. But staying in Butte was too risky. By now, the Butte Police would be looking for him, as would Milo Ivankovich and his enforcers. Neither would take kindly to someone skipping out on their debts. Nick left several bills for the bar unpaid, and likely the creditors would be contacting the police soon. Ivankovich was already furious and would not hesitate to send someone looking for him. For the moment, he needed to get far away from Butte until he could get things figured out. Contacting Theresa was out of the question, although he was not sure he wanted to anyway. Their relationship hadn't been good for the past several months. The stress of debt and working together had been more than either of them anticipated. They hadn't been intimate in months, and other than work issues, they hadn't talked much at all. They rarely spent much time together outside of work. It had been pretty clear to both of them for a few months that things had not worked out in the business or their relationship. He hated to leave her alone to deal with the business debt and Ivankovich but didn't see any alternative. He had to do what he felt was best for him, and that was to take the money and run.

Nick has been gone four days since seeing Ivankovich at the bar and leaving Butte with the money. Not quite sure where to go, he had headed north through Helena and onto Great Falls. The roads were snow-packed and icy in parts, especially up through the small towns of Basin and Boulder. Following along the Boulder River, the road was winding and steep in places as it courses along the Continental Divide. Travel was slow on the two-lane highway, and several times he was slowed by drifting snow across the road. When he reached Helena, the winds had picked up even more substantial, but he decided to go on to Great Falls to distance himself from Butte a little further. Exhausted, he found a cheap motel on the south side of town, had a meal of chicken fried steak with a couple of Oly beers to wash it down, and then settled in for the night.

He slept until around 8 o'clock, showered, and then got some breakfast of two poached eggs, bacon, and toast. He read the morning Great Falls Tribune but saw nothing regarding the Belmont Bar or his disappearance. Scanning the headlines of The Montana Standard, the Butte paper, there it was on page five, "Proprietor of Butte's Belmont Bar Disappears." The article was short but detailed the failure to pay the Belmont's bills and the disappearance of the money he and his partner/wife had set aside for the bar. The article had no picture of Nick but said the police wanted him for questioning. A quote by the police detective simply said, "We are looking for Nick Evans to discuss it. If anyone knows his whereabouts, please contact the Butte police department."

They must know about the $600, he thought to himself. Either Theresa knew of the money before him taking it or Mickey McCarthy had gone to the police. Ivankovich would not have gone to the police, but surely, he had his enforcers on the lookout for him. Whichever the case, Nick needed to lay low for a while. He considered continuing north to Canada where he could escape safely, but he wasn't ready to do that yet. Nick had some unfinished business to take care of before leaving. No, he would buy some time, let things calm down, then execute his plan.

Chapter 30

Butte

"What do you mean you can't find him? Where the hell is he?" asked Ivankovich.

"I don't know," replied Cabby. "I have searched all over Butte and have asked around, but no one has seen him."

"Have you talked with his wife?'

"Well, sort of."

"What do you mean, sort of?"

"I have talked with her but not directly about Evans. I didn't want to scare her off. But I am meeting her for drinks and dancing Saturday night. I plan to get more information from her then."

"You had better. I want Nick Evans found, my money repaid, and a clear message sent. I don't care what you have to do to get it. Do you understand?"

"Yes, sir. I will find out where he is and get your money. It just may take a little time and some patience."

"I don't have much patience, and what little I have is nearly gone. Get Nick Evans!"

The snow had been falling nearly all day, accumulating another few inches. The cold wind continued to blow, so there were very few people on the streets. Cabby was concerned that Theresa would not show. He considered going by the Empire to pick her up but decided against it. Young didn't want to be too forward and scare her off. On the other hand, he knew Ivankovich was not a patient man, so he had to get information soon. Whatever it took, he needed to see Theresa Evans tonight and get information about her husband's whereabouts.

Much to his surprise, as he turned the corner from Wyoming onto Galena, Theresa was walking away from The Empire toward Montana Street and Maloney's bar. At first, he wasn't sure it was her since she was wearing a long coat, scarf, and hat to protect her from the cold wind. But he recognized her walk. Maloney's was only a couple blocks, but it was a challenge in this weather. It would have been easy for her to cancel, but she didn't. Cabby took it as an excellent sign. Pulling alongside, he said, "Hop in, it's too cold to be walking tonight." Theresa smiled a wide smile then slid in alongside Cabby in the front seat.

Once inside the bar, they had a few drinks and talked about a variety of things. She told him about her years growing up in Anaconda, her marriage to Nick, and their time operating the Belmont and all involved with it. Theresa didn't mention her other marriages or her children, not wanting to scare him off. With each additional drink, the conversation became more personal and open. The bartender brought Cabby another Oly beer and Theresa a shot of whiskey. As he set them down and walked away, Cabby seized the opportunity. "So what happened with your husband, what was his name, Nick?"

"It's a long and complicated story," replied Theresa.

"Suffice it to say that we are no longer together, and there is no chance we will get back together."

"I am very sorry to hear that. Any idea where your husband may have gone?"

"No idea. I doubt I will ever hear from Nick again. I am sure he took the money and is long gone."

They sat in silence for a few minutes, then Cabby said, "If there is anything I can do to help, I would be happy to do so."

"Thanks, but I don't think there is anything anyone can do to help."

Chapter 31

Whoever said April showers bring May flowers never lived in Butte in the spring. April showers may very well be snow. At an elevation of nearly a mile, the nights in April are still cold, and daytime temperatures aren't typically hot. The average daily high in April is 48 degrees, and the average low 36 degrees. But this wasn't a typical or average Butte April. The days had been chilly, and there had been a few snow flurries the past few days. Every night that week, temperatures dropped below freezing. It didn't seem as though warm weather ever would arrive.

Theresa and Cabby had been seeing each other for several weeks now and had gradually become close. Theresa was living at The Empire and found work as a barmaid at Maloney's. It didn't pay particularly well, but the tips were decent, and she was getting by, though barely. Theresa had been sharing a room with a friend, Roberta Graham, for the past couple of weeks to help share expenses. One day she approached the managing clerk, Harry Hustor. Cabby was with her.

"Harry, this is my new honey, Cabby Young. Cabby, this is Harry," Theresa said enthusiastically.

"Pleased to meet you," said Cabby.

Harry looked up but didn't respond.

"Harry, I would like to get a single room now that I have a new honey. Is there anything available?"

"Room #9 is available. Marion moved out a couple of

days ago to #6 across the hall."

"Great. I will take it." And just like that, Theresa had a place of her own – a place where she was able to entertain if she chose to do so. And with her new relationship with Cabby Young, she was hoping to have some privacy soon.

***

Mickey continued with her life as usual. She had adjusted well to the physical nature of work in the Anselmo Mine, but it bothered her to be underground. Her disguise as a man had been adequate, but she remained concerned that she would be exposed, either by Nick Evans, should he reappear in Butte, or by Theresa Evans. Mickey was still not sure whether Theresa knew, but she was always on guard and regularly kept a close eye on Theresa. As far as Mickey could tell, Theresa hadn't told anyone, but she remained vigilant. The first few weeks after her meeting with Theresa, Mickey was very anxious. Still, as time had progressed, she had been a bit less so. Nonetheless, she couldn't assume anything about what Theresa might know, and certainly couldn't let her guard down. Mickey had observed Theresa with Cabby Young on several occasions, which led her to believe that Nick Evans had not contacted her and was likely nowhere in the area. For that, she was thankful. But she couldn't let go of the possibility that he told Theresa, and she was just waiting for the right time to expose her or blackmail her.

Chapter 32

Return to Butte

Since leaving Butte nearly three months ago, Nick had been laying low in Great Falls. He found work in a local bar, changed his name to Michael Orlov, and had been very careful not to bring unnecessary attention to himself. He had considered continuing north to Canada, maybe even returning to Bulgaria, but something just wouldn't let him. That something, or someone, was Theresa Evans. He thought it would be easy to take the money, run, and start a new life elsewhere. But now he realized he didn't want to do that without Theresa. He loved her much more than he realized.

Maybe, just maybe, she would come away with him. If he could just get her alone and explain himself, she might understand. Surely she still loved him even though she was undoubtedly upset with him for leaving. Of course, they wouldn't be able to stay in Butte. It would be too risky there. But there were lots of places they could go to resume their life together. He just needed to have some time alone with Theresa to convince her. He decided he must find a way they could be together.

After arriving in Great Falls, Nick had grown a Cary Grant-style mustache and changed his hairstyle. While in Butte, he was always clean-shaven, and hair without a part combed forward with bangs nearly to his eyebrows. He had typically let it go naturally with no product to hold it in place. Now his hairstyle was much shorter, parted on the right side and combed back, held in place by styling cream that made it look much darker than it was. It was quite remarkable how much the changes had altered his appearance. A few changes in clothing and ten extra pounds, he looked like a different man. He was confident that he looked much different than Nick Evans, who lived in Butte. "Michael Orlov" had little resemblance to Nick Evans. It had been quite easy to get away with it in Great Falls with people that didn't know him, but fooling people in Butte who did know him was a different story. If he had any chance of getting Theresa back, he had to take the risk.

After gathering his belongings from the apartment, he had been living in, Nick loaded his car and began his return trip to Butte. Nearing the small town of Boulder, he decided he had better give his new identity a trial run. On his journey to Great Falls a couple of months ago, Nick had stopped at a gas station in Boulder. Hopeful that the same young man was working, he put his plan to the test. Sure enough, the same young man approached his car just as he was stepping out.

"Good afternoon, sir," said the young man.

"Fill it up and check the oil," Nick responded, being careful to conceal his Bulgarian accent as much as possible. He watched the young man closely for any indication that he recognized him from his previous trip. Though it was a couple of months ago, Boulder is a small town and likely didn't have many outsiders stop for fuel. Nick reasoned that most would easily make it from Helena to Butte on a full tank, so it was mainly the locals who used the station. The occasional outsider would likely be recognized if they returned.

The young man fueled the tank and checked the oil but gave no indication he recognized Nick. After closing the hood, he said, "Nice car. We don't see too many of these here in Boulder. Maybe a couple every two or three months."

Was he recalling seeing him and his car, Nick wondered? Not likely, but certainly possible.

Hoping to give the impression he had never been through the area before, Nick said, "Can you give me directions to Butte? I am traveling from Great Falls to Billings but want to spend a day or two in Butte first. I have heard it is a fascinating place."

After getting directions from the young man, Nick pulled out of the station watching through his rearview mirror for any indication that the man was suspicious or recognized him. The man simply waved and turned to service a car that had just pulled in. So far, so good. The first test passed, but the next test would be much more difficult. Next stop – Butte and his old neighborhood.

Chapter 33

Butte

"Well, any progress?" Ivankovich asked Cabby somewhat angrily.

"Not really. Theresa has given no indication she has heard from him or knows where he might be. It looks as though she has moved on from him."

"I want him found, and I want my money. Do you understand?"

"I am doing everything I can to find out. What more do you want me to do?"

"I don't care what you must do. Just find Evans and get my money!

Young had been seeing Theresa regularly now for about six weeks. He didn't have any real feelings for her. It was just part of the "job," but Cabby grew tired of the whole thing. He would like just to walk away from it, but he was in too deep now, and Ivankovich wouldn't allow it. He had paid him a stipend for his work so far and would want it back if he quit. And Cabby had already spent that money and was counting on more. It was time to get more aggressive. He needed to either find out where Nick Evans was or put an end to it. The whole thing was wearing him out.

"Theresa, how about going out to the Belmont tomorrow night for some drinks?" Cabby asked.

"You know I don't like to go there anymore. The

memories are still painful, and I feel like everyone stares at me, knowing all that has happened."

"But they have some good music, and it's been quite a while. Let's just give it a try. Tomorrow is Wednesday, so it shouldn't be too busy. If you aren't feeling comfortable and enjoying yourself, we can always leave and go elsewhere."

Reluctantly Theresa agreed. She was still a little uncomfortable going to the Belmont, but for a chance to spend the evening with Cabby, she was willing. Theresa hoped that it would turn into something much more than their other dates together.

Cabby determined that tomorrow night would be the night to get the information for finding Nick Evans from Theresa. He couldn't wait much longer. Surely after a few drinks, dancing, and intimate talking, she would provide him the information he needed. If not, he would have to resort to other means of getting the information from her.

Chapter 34

Edward Deanne had been a friend of Cabby Young's for many years. Like Cabby, Deanne had bounced around from job to job. While Cabby was a cook, Deanne was a bartender, currently at the Belmont Bar. He had started work at the Belmont just before Nick disappearing and Theresa losing the bar. Since Theresa had hired him, she was familiar with him and his background. What Theresa didn't know was that Deanne and Young were friends. Young would often meet Deanne after his shift was over, and they occasionally spent time together on their days off. Since Deanne had been working at the Belmont at the time of Nick's disappearance, he had observed several things in those final days. For instance, Deanne was aware that Nick put money away in the bar's office though he didn't see exactly where. Deanne also knew that Nick and Theresa were not getting along very well.

Deanne had been just getting to the bar the afternoon that Ivankovich had confronted Theresa about the money owed him. He certainly didn't know the details, but he could put the pieces together. Ivankovich had loaned them a sum of money, they had not been making payments, he wanted his money back, and he was angry.

Sitting at the Mecca Cafe enjoying breakfast, Deanne said to Cabby, "So what's the deal with you and Ivankovich?"

"I do some freelance work for him on occasion. Why

do you ask?"

"Does it have anything to do with the Belmont?"

Before he answered, Cabby thought for a few minutes. It wasn't Deanne's business, but maybe he could help find Nick. Maybe he knew something that would help locate him. Perhaps he heard or saw something that would be of help.

"It does, as a matter of fact. Ivankovich hired me to find Nick Evans and get some of his money back."

"Is that right? How is the search going?"

"Not very well. Nick Evans seems to have disappeared into thin air, and no one seems to have any idea where he has gone."

"Ahh, now I see why you have been spending time with Theresa Evans. Well, maybe I can help you out. I overheard and saw a few things before he took off. I don't know where he went, but I might be able to help you find out."

"That would be great," replied Young excitedly.

"But it will cost you. I want a cut of whatever Ivankovich is paying you."

"Fair enough. If you help me find Nick, I will gladly share my pay. At this point, I am not getting anywhere. We plan to come to the Belmont tomorrow night for drinks. Maybe you can help find out something helpful then."

Chapter 35

The man in the corner of the Belmont Bar had been watching Theresa for several days now. Waiting, planning. Tonight, he was dressed in grey trousers and a white button-down shirt, a fedora pulled down low on his head, and dark glasses which he casually peered over as he observed. He had been sitting in the corner near the card players while casually watching Theresa with Cabby. He had changed his appearance since he was last in Butte. He was now sporting a Carey Grant style mustache, slicked-back short hair, and an additional ten pounds. He had never needed glasses for vision, but these helped to conceal his appearance. He was confident that he would go unrecognized by Theresa and others.

Watching her with this man tonight had made him increasingly mad. He wasn't sure what to expect really, but now that he had seen her with him a couple of times, he had become angry. Or maybe it was jealousy? Whatever it was, he didn't like it. Getting her alone and then convincing her to run away with him would be much more complicated than he initially expected.

Mickey was sitting near the end of the bar, not too far from where Theresa and Cabby sat. She was near enough to overhear their conversation but not too close that they suspected she was eavesdropping. Mickey was still concerned that Nick told Theresa about her secret. Not knowing for sure, Mickey was very eager and anxious to find out. Most of the conversation she overheard was mundane – nothing of interest until she heard Theresa say something to Cabby that was very concerning.

"There is something I have wanted to tell you for a while," she said to Cabby. "I know something, a secret that I haven't told anyone. I have been considering for weeks now if I should go to the police with it. Or if I should just forget about it. But it weighs very heavily on me."

"What is it? Maybe I can help you decide what to do," replied Cabby.

"I am not sure if I should say anything. It could get someone into serious trouble."

"At least tell me who it involves."

Theresa thought for a few minutes. "I can't tell you much here, but maybe when we are alone. I can tell you it has to do with my husband Nick and a person I saw him having a serious discussion with a short time before he disappeared."

Mickey sat up straight in her chair but couldn't believe her ears. Did she hear that correctly? Was Theresa referring to her discussion with Nick? She must know her secret. But why hasn't Theresa told anyone yet, and why would Theresa share it with this guy? If she were going to reveal Mickey's secret to Cabby, it would serve no purpose other than receiving some advice. And who knows what he would advise or do with the information. He might suggest she go straight to the police. Convinced now that she knows her identity secret, she thought to herself, and I can't allow that to happen.

A short distance away, bartender Ed Deanne has also been listening and watching as much as possible without making it apparent he was eavesdropping. He, too, heard Theresa talk about a secret she knew. Deanne wasn't sure what the secret was but was confident it would help them find Nick Evans. If Cabby was able to get Theresa alone, she was sure to share the whereabouts of Nick if she knew where he was.

"I am not sure I am ready to tell you yet," Theresa said to Cabby. "Let me think about it a little more. Maybe we can come back again tomorrow night. We can dance, have a few drinks, and then maybe I will share with you the secret that has been on my mind." Theresa was not sure if she genuinely wanted to share what she knew with Cabby. Still, she had been becoming increasingly fond of him, which would allow her to take their relationship to the next level. And besides, coming back to the Belmont wasn't that bad. In all honesty, it was quite enjoyable. She was already looking forward to some intimacy with Cabby Young.

Chapter 36

Thursday happened to be payday for the miners, so it was very busy at the Belmont. They were always eager for fun on paydays, which usually led to drinking, dancing, and music. Patrons sat along the mahogany bar while others stood nearby, trying to attract the bartender's attention. In the corner, a piano player entertained with swing and jazz music such as Glen Miller and Billie Holiday tunes. While some filled the dance floor, others played cards in the rear of the bar. Cigarette smoke filled the air, and the noise of laughter and banter overwhelmed the barmaids as they attempted to serve the many patrons.

Entering the front door, Theresa scanned the bar for several minutes before locking onto her new "honey," as she now called him. It was the first time she had returned to the Belmont Bar at a time when so many of her previous patrons were there. Theresa was a bit apprehensive, knowing many of them were aware they had lost the bar. Dressed in a pale blue knee-length dress with high heels, red lipstick, and a bow in her medium brown wavy hair, she was ready to make her move. At 5'6" and 145 pounds, Theresa was beautiful and had never had difficulty attracting men. Casually working her way across the dance floor, she approached the man sitting at the bar. "Care to buy a lady a drink?" she said to the rough-looking man sitting by himself. Dressed in tan trousers and a white short-sleeved collared shirt, the man had come eager to spend some time with Theresa. He was tired but looking forward to some fun and companionship. More importantly, he was anxious to hear her secret in hopes it would lead him to find Nick Evans. He looked her over, smiled widely, and replied, "It would be my honor. What's your pleasure?"

"Well, I am a whiskey kind of lady, and make it a double, the night is young." As the bartender delivered the drinks, she leaned in seductively, rested her hand on his thigh, and whispered into his ear. "I think tonight is going to be a great night."

Cabby Young smiled and replied, "I certainly hope so!"

Cabby had worked as a cook in several of Butte's restaurants over the past few years. He had bounced from one job to another, never settling into a long-term job. He had refused to consider working in the mines. The work was too dirty and dangerous for him. No, he preferred the safety of being above ground. Now at 46 years old, mining was out of the question anyway. Cabby had never married, though he had had several lady friends. A few weeks ago, he met this beautiful woman, and their relationship had been growing closer every day though his motive was undoubtedly not romantic initially. Theresa was significantly younger, only 38, but they seemed to have hit it off very well. They had not yet become intimate, and although he was not opposed, maybe that was what it would take for him to get the information from her. Based on her comments a couple of days ago, she was hopeful that tonight would be the night that they would. He and Theresa had been spending more and more time together, so it seemed natural that they took it to the next level. However, she didn't realize that his primary motivation was to get information about Nick Evans from her. If that meant faking a deeper level of interest in her, then so be it.

A few drinks later and after several dances, Theresa made her move. As they headed back to the bar, she suddenly feigned rolling her ankle and nearly fell to the floor. She would have had she not reached out to grab the arm of Cabby.

"Are you all right?" he asked, as she clutched his arm.

"I think I sprained my ankle," Theresa replied.

"Let me help you to the chair so I can take a look." There was no immediate swelling or discoloration, but when he touched it, Theresa cried out in manufactured pain. After several minutes she said, "I think I need to lie down for a while. Could you help me to my room; it is just down the block."

The man had been watching from the corner of the bar, careful not to draw attention to himself. It would have been disastrous if recognized by her or anyone else. He watched Cabby take Theresa by the arm and guide her out the front door into the cold evening. He then paid his tab and followed at a safe distance, taking care not to be noticed by anyone, especially Theresa and Cabby.

The night air was crisp, and the street was quiet except for a few patrons standing outside smoking cigarettes. A few ladies walking from the Empire Hotel to the Belmont approached them and offered a greeting. Margaret Bowers and Marion Grant both knew Theresa. Marion moved into the Empire about a month before and lived across the hall from Theresa. They weren't friends, but they had spoken a few times. Margaret was a friend of Marion's, but Theresa had only met her once. After the brief greeting, Theresa and her new friend walked down Mercury Street arm in arm with Theresa limping on her ankle.

The man continued following at a distance but was careful not to be seen or heard. He avoided eye contact with the two women as they passed, hoping that they wouldn't attempt to engage him and expose his presence to Theresa and Cabby.

As they arrived at the Empire, Theresa reached into her purse to get her key. Clerk Harry Hustor, an employee of Ivankovich, observed them entering the hotel but paid them little attention though he certainly was aware of their presence. Hustor smiled to himself when realizing it was Young who accompanied Theresa. He had seen this scenario several times before. Finally, maybe Young was getting somewhere with her. Hustor noted the time. In the corner near the fireplace sat a couple snuggling close and enjoying the warmth. They also took little notice. By this time of night, only a few patrons remained at the Empire's bar. Old Mr. Walsh had had far too much to drink, and the bartender was encouraging him to go home, but it was doubtful he could do so unassisted. Three others were in the corner playing cards, too focused on the game to even notice.

Theresa and Cabby walked past the bar to the base of the staircase. As she grabbed the handrail, it creaked, and the young couple briefly looked up and then resumed their kissing in front of the fireplace. The card players gave no indication they heard anything. Theresa wrapped her arm around him as she began to climb the stairs to her room on the second floor. Cabby assisted her into her room, and after unlocking the door, he helped her to her bed.

"Will you be all right for a few minutes? I need to use the restroom, and then I will take a look at your ankle."

"I will be fine, it's feeling much better already. I'll just sit here on the bed until you return. The restroom is down the hall and to the right."

As Cabby walked away, Theresa smiled as she watched him close the door before he disappeared into the hallway. For several minutes she contemplated all that has happened over the past several months. The loss of their money and, subsequently, the bar. Then, Nick's disappearance, her move to the Empire, and now her new "honey." She hadn't felt this happy for a long time now. Maybe things were about to improve. She had been through so many difficulties. It was about time that things started looking up.

Theresa was momentarily startled as she heard the doorknob turning. She had been sitting on the bed staring out the window, lost in her thoughts for quite some time, and had momentarily forgotten about Cabby leaving to go to the restroom. Still looking out the window and facing away from the door, Theresa said,

"Come on in, honey." She heard the door close and then footsteps, but when there was no response, she turned toward the door. And before she could react, she felt a sharp blow to the left side of her head, and then everything went dark.

Chapter 37

Jack Duggan had worked his way up through the Butte Police Department over the past 20 years. Now nearly 50, he felt like he had seen and heard just about everything. As a street cop, he had dealt with all kinds of misdemeanors such as petty theft, public indecency, bar fights, and the like. His ability to deal effectively with the working class had given him a very positive reputation in Butte. Miners, service workers, retail workers all knew and respected Jack. He had always been considered a fair and honest policeman. Of course, this had naturally led to various privileges and promotions over the years. Nearly two years ago, he moved into detectives, primarily due to his reputation and knowledge of the locals. He mainly worked evenings since most of the crime occurred after sundown. Last night he was particularly busy in downtown Butte. He had investigated a couple of reported robberies and a bar fight where a miner had beaten another man over a heated discussion regarding the labor unions' role. Other patrons had taken sides quickly, and a huge battle ensued. By the time he finished, it was well past 2 a.m. when he got home. He was exhausted and quickly fell asleep.

The sound of a phone ringing startled Jack. Already 9 a.m., he felt like he had just gone to bed. "Hello," he said as he picked up the receiver groggily.

"Jack, you better get over here right away," said John Murphy, one of the officers from the station.

"This better be important," Duggan said. "This is supposed to be my day off."

"I know, sir, but there has been an incident over at the Empire Hotel, an apparent beating, and it looks like there is a good chance the victim may not make it," Murphy explained.

"Any suspects?" Duggan asked.

"Yes, but whereabouts unknown. Our men are looking for him now."

"You got a name?"

"DC Young," he replied.

Duggan had known Cabby Young for about ten years. A cook who had worked at several local restaurants and bars, Young had been in and out of trouble. Mostly small things – petty theft, fighting, associating with the ladies over at Pleasant Alley. As far as Duggan knew, Young had never gotten into serious trouble, but the local police knew him well from his frequent indiscretions. Duggan suspected involvement with more significant crimes via his relationship with Milo Ivankovich, but so far, he had managed to stay clean.

"I will be right there," Duggan said. "See if you can get any information on the whereabouts of Young."

Marian Grant lived in room #6 at The Empire. She had been working as a seamstress for a year or so, but business was slow. Marian began residing at the Empire several weeks before, believing that it would be temporary, and eventually, would be able to move to a place with a better reputation. She recognized that living adjacent to Pleasant Alley and across from the brothels was not ideal, but as soon as work picked up, she would be able to move on. Marian was not naive. Many of the female boarders here were making their living in the red-light district, but she was determined to get out as soon as possible. Marian met Theresa a couple of weeks ago when Theresa was sharing a room with Roberta Graham, a waitress at the nearby M&M. Last week Theresa moved to room #9 so that she would have a private room. Number 6 was across the hall and down one door from Theresa's place. Although they were not close, Marian had taken a liking to Theresa, and they frequently had coffee together and visited. Last night, they shared a drink in Theresa's room before going out for the evening.

After receiving the call, Duggan headed straight to the hospital. He wanted to see the victim before going to the Empire. Two nurses told Duggan that she had been unresponsive since arriving. They brought Duggan to Theresa's room, and he was shocked by what he saw. Lying in a hospital bed, clearly cleaned up a bit, but she was still frothing at the mouth and moaning unintelligently. There was bruising on her face, breasts, and legs. Duggan was no doctor, but it seemed clear to him that she was not likely to live much longer. It was very likely he would be handling a homicide case soon.

After leaving the hospital, Duggan drove to the Empire to examine the scene and talk with witnesses. He met with Marian Grant and Roberta Graham. Both residents were at the Empire when the beating occurred.

"Miss Grant, tell me what you recall happened this morning," instructed Duggan.

"At 7:15 this morning, I was walking down the hall to the shared bathroom. As I approached Theresa's room, I stopped, intending to invite her for coffee. I noticed Theresa's door slightly ajar and moaning coming from inside. I knocked, awaited a response, but when none came, I entered the room."

"And what did you see?" asked Duggan.

"Theresa was lying on the bed frothing from the mouth. I yelled, "Oh my God, Theresa, are you okay?" I saw her severely swollen face, and she had multiple bruises and traces of blood on her face and neck. I ran back into the hallway, looking for someone who could help. At the far end, I saw a figure, hurriedly walking away."

Who was it that you saw?

"It was Cabby Young!" I yelled at Young. "Quick, go get a doctor. Theresa is very sick and needs help right away."

"Did Young respond?" asked Duggan.

"Yes. Young said, 'Okay, You stay with her, and I'll go get a doctor.'" Marian said she remained with Theresa, but Young didn't return for nearly two hours. "'Where is the doctor?' I asked when he returned. He replied, 'I couldn't find one. I went to Dr. William's office, but he wasn't there. I couldn't find any other doctors either.'"

"What happened next?" coaxed Duggan.

"Exasperated, I went to the hotel office and called Dr. Williams's home. He immediately came to the hotel and called for an ambulance to take Theresa to the county hospital. After a brief examination, Dr. Williams said, 'She sustained a brain injury from a blow to the head, and I doubt she will make it through the day.' He told me to call the police and the County Commissioners. When I called the police, they told me to call the county doctor, and that Detective Duggan would be there shortly. The commissioners' office said that she should be sent to the hospital at once and sent over Dot Kiley from the welfare office."

Marian couldn't believe what had happened. Last night, she saw her before she left for the evening, helping her button her dress and enjoyed a drink together. Theresa had been okay and was in good spirits. Now she was in bad shape and may not make it through the day, according to the doctor.

Roberta Graham had little to offer. She said that she was a waitress and currently unemployed. Roberta had been Theresa's roommate before moving to her room a few days ago but had not talked with her since, other than seeing her walking with Young last night. She was not around last night when the incident occurred. She was in her apartment this morning but said she didn't hear or see anything.

Duggan then questioned Harry Hustor, the clerk at the Empire last night.

"I don't know, didn't see or hear anything. A woman just came to my office and asked me to call the doctor," he replied.

"When did Theresa Evans move into her current

room?"

"About four days ago. Ms. Evans said she had a 'new honey' and wanted to have a single room."

"Do you know who this new honey is?"

"DC Young. She introduced him to me the day she asked for a new apartment."

"Did you see Theresa yesterday at all?"

"Yes. We greeted each other, but that is about all."

"Did you notice anything unusual? Maybe bruises on her face?"

"No, I didn't see any."

"Did you see DC Young yesterday?"

"I have seen them together three or four times now, but I don't recall if I saw them yesterday."

"You didn't see him last night?"

"No."

"When did you first know there was trouble in Theresa's room?"

"When that woman, Marian Grant, came to the office around 10 o'clock and asked me to call a doctor."

"You didn't hear any noise or commotion?"

"No. My office is on the other side of the hotel, off of Wyoming Street. Her room is on the Galena Street side of the building."

Duggan had the feeling that Hustor knew more than what he was saying. The Empire was the type of place people didn't want outsiders to know all that was going on there. Whether by choice or because he hadn't honestly heard anything, Hustor was not about to share anything additional about what had occurred last night.

Chapter 38

Duggan had talked to Marian Grant, Roberta Graham, and Harry Hustor. All of them were at the Empire this morning. The only one he hadn't talked to yet was Cabby Young. Young had disappeared, and no one seemed to know where he went, so Duggan called dispatch to alert all officers to be on the lookout for Young.

Duggan then went to several places where Young was known to frequent, but he wasn't at any of them. Duggan left word that he was looking for Young and if anyone saw or heard from Young to contact the police department.

About two hours later, he got a call from Young.

"Detective Duggan, this Cabby Young. I understand that you have been looking for me. What is it about?" Young sounded a bit strange to Duggan. Like maybe he had been drinking. He seemed a bit confused.

"Come up to the station, and we will talk about it," instructed Duggan.

A short time later, Young arrived, and Duggan took him into the office. He looked a mess. His hair was uncombed, eyes bloodshot, and clothes wrinkled as though he had been wearing them for several days. Duggan studied him for several minutes, noting his demeanor and the look of anxiety in his eyes.

"Where were you last night?" Duggan asked.

"I was with Theresa Evans last evening and then

went to the Belmont Bar to visit my friend who was bartending there."

Duggan noted that Young was slurring his words a bit and seemed confused. He didn't sound as though he was confident about what he was saying. He had been drinking, but it wasn't clear how much or how recently.

"You didn't return to the Empire after visiting your friend?" Duggan asked.

"I had been back with Theresa again, but then about two in the morning, I left to look for a doctor."

"Why did you go looking for a doctor?"

"Theresa was sick or something. I didn't know what was wrong with her. A lady at the hotel told me to go get a doctor."

"And did you get one, a doctor?"

"I couldn't find one, so I came back to the hotel."

"What time did you come back?'

"I think it was about seven or eight o'clock."

"Why didn't you call the police?"

"I didn't know what happened to her."

Things were not adding up. Either Young was lying, confused, or there was someone else involved. Until Duggan knew more, he needed to keep Young in custody. There was ample evidence to hold him.

Chapter 39

Before this week, it had been three and a half months since Nick Evans saw his wife, Theresa. When he left, he had no intention of returning. Nick had taken their entire savings and the money from the loan from Mickey and ran. He had seen no way out. He couldn't pay off the bills, nor could he pay the money he owed to Ivankovich. And surely Ivankovich and his enforcers were looking for him. Even now, he disguised himself to keep from being recognized while back in Butte. He was sure no one could tell he was Nick Evans, but he needed to be very cautious.

Last night, seeing Theresa with another man caused him to be both jealous and angry. He didn't think it would affect him quite so much. After all, he was the one who left with no explanation and no way to be contacted. For all Theresa knew, he disappeared forever and would never be back. After this much time, she had no reason to believe he was coming back. It should be easy to understand that she would move on. But it wasn't. He realizes now that it was a mistake to take the money and run without her. But there was no turning back now. Jealousy and anger had taken over.

When Theresa and Young had left the Belmont last night, walking arm and arm, he could hardly contain himself – just seeing his wife with another man fueled his anger and jealousy. The more he watched them, the angrier and more jealous he became. Nick didn't know what to do or if there was anything to do given the circumstances. So, he followed them. Quietly and at a safe distance, he followed them as they left the Belmont and walked arm in arm toward the Empire. As Theresa and Cabby entered through the Galena Street entrance, Nick quickly went around and entered on Wyoming Street. The clerk busied himself in the office and didn't notice him as he came in and headed up the stairs. Just as Nick was about to reach the intersection of the two hallways connecting the hotel's wings, he heard footsteps. Quickly ducking into an open doorway, he saw Young turn into the restroom. Once out of sight, Nick turned down the hallway and headed in the direction of room #9.

If I can get her alone for a few minutes, I can convince her to run away with me, Nick thought to himself while walking down the hall toward Theresa's room. Likely, Nick had only a short time before Young would return. But would Theresa even want to leave? Thinking back to seeing them together earlier in the evening, Nick recalled how close they seemed. Maybe Theresa has already moved on. Even if Nick were to have some time with Theresa, she might reject him. Is it possible she loved this other man now? The thought of it filled him with anger.

Chapter 40

Sitting at the bar at the Belmont last night, Mickey had overheard the conversation between Theresa and Cabby. It was clear to her that tonight, Theresa was planning to share a secret she knew involving Nick. Was it the secret he knew about Mickey's identity? She couldn't be sure, nor could she take any chances that others would find out about her. She had far too much invested to have it revealed now. She had heard Theresa say she had a secret to share but couldn't tell him in public, but she would when they were alone. They headed for the Empire, she was sure. Mickey had known for quite some time that Theresa moved into the Empire after losing the bar, and her apartment shared with Nick. But what would she do, could she do, if Theresa told Cabby of her secret life?

Mickey contemplated what it all meant. Did Theresa honestly know her secret, and would she tell Young? And if she did, what would Young do with the information? Mickey knew Young to be a bit of a hustler, knew that he did work on the side for Ivankovich. She wouldn't be surprised if that were what Young was doing now, digging up information for Ivankovich. The stakes were just too high, Mickey decided. She didn't know what she would do if Theresa told him. She had to try to stop her from doing so. It was time for her to act. She jumped off the barstool, headed out the door, and toward the Empire.

Following Young and Theresa out of the Belmont Bar and toward the Empire Hotel, she couldn't help but notice the man strolling behind the couple. At first, she thought nothing of it, assuming he was leaving the bar and going home. But then she became suspicious when he slowed down each time that the couple did. She realized that he was concealing himself from their view. And there was something very familiar about the man's gait. She couldn't quite put her finger on it, but she was sure she had seen that gait before. As they neared the Empire, the couple entered through the Galena Street entrance, but the man continued and turned the corner at Wyoming Street. Mickey quickly got there, and just as she did, she saw the man enter the Empire through the other entrance. Then it hit her. The gait was that of Nick Evans.

Mickey was shocked to see Evans. No one had seen him in Butte for quite some time, and most assumed him to be long gone from the area. She certainly had not heard from him since she paid him the second $300 that they had agreed upon to keep her identity a secret from others. What was he doing back in Butte? Why was he following Theresa and Young? He was clearly up to something. Following him into the Empire Hotel, she was determined to find out what he was doing there. She was sure that he hadn't noticed her following him or them.

Once inside, she watched Nick turn the corner and head down the hallway. Just as she started to follow,

Mickey heard the sound of footsteps coming from the other direction. Ducking into an open doorway, Mickey listened carefully. She expected a conversation but heard none. Stepping back into the hall, Mickey saw a man turn into what appeared to be a restroom. She wasn't able to identify the man but didn't think it was Nick. Looking up and down the hall, she saw no sign of Nick. He had disappeared. Deciding that he couldn't be far, she chose to hide in the open doorway and wait to see if he would reappear. She wasn't sure how long she had been waiting and listening, but it must have been 15 minutes or more. Then suddenly she heard footsteps again. And these were quickly moving footsteps. Sticking her head out into the hall, she had a glimpse of a man beginning the descent of the staircase leading to the Wyoming Street exit. On the other end, she saw Young looking confused and anxious. He was hurrying back toward the Galena Street exit. Not sure what was going on, Mickey decided to follow after the first man whom she now understood to be Nick Evans.

Looking north on Wyoming Street, Mickey saw Nick walking very quickly. He wasn't entirely running but the closest thing to it. For an April evening in Butte, the moon and stars were bright, making visibility pretty good. At 35 degrees, it felt much colder with the steady, brisk wind blowing. Mickey followed but struggled to keep up. She saw Nick turn west at the corner, so she hurried so that he was not out of sight for long. He then turned north on Main and ducked into the M and M Bar just as Mickey got to the corner. Nick had no idea anyone was following him. He hadn't noticed Mickey follow him into or out of the Empire. Nick had hurried away, only glancing back a couple of times but didn't see Mickey a safe distance behind. He now settled onto a bar stool, took a long and deep breath, and ordered a beer.

"Is this seat taken?" came the voice from behind him. It was a familiar voice, one that he hadn't heard for quite some time. And a voice he didn't care to hear ever again. Turning, he asked, "What do you want, Mickey?"

"It's nice to see you again, too," she replied sarcastically.

"I don't have time for this."

"I think you had better make time. I followed you from the Empire. I think we better have a little talk."

Nick was shocked as well as a little panicked. What did she mean she followed me from the Empire? He didn't see her. And what did she see? He was careful not to show any outward reaction to what he was feeling inside.

"Not here, somewhere a little more private," he replied.

"I don't think it can wait, Nick. How about the table near the back? There isn't anyone close enough to hear us."

Once at the table, he looked over his shoulder to make sure no one was close enough to hear he said, "OK, what do you want?"

"So, what is going on, Nick? The last time I saw or heard from you, you took the remainder of the money we agreed upon, and I presume skipped town. I had heard you were long gone only to see you tonight, albeit in disguise, following your wife from the Belmont to the Empire. I figured my secret was safe, though I did worry you told Theresa. I have been watching her closely for any sign that she knew, and then I saw her tonight with that Young fellow. I overheard them talking about a secret she knew, a secret that she intended to tell him, and I was afraid it was about me. So I followed them out of the Belmont. That's when I saw you following them. At first, I didn't know it was you, with the disguise and all, but when I watched you walk, I recognized that gait. I knew it had to be you. So I followed you into the Empire."

Immediately Nick began to perspire and a worried look surfaced. What had she seen? What does she believe she saw? "I, I... I don't know what to say. I had to come back to find out what was happening with Theresa. Yes, I took the money – the money from you, the bar. At least what remained of it. I had lost some of it gambling, and there was no way we could pay the bills or pay Ivankovich back. The only choice I felt that I had was to leave, and my relationship with Theresa wasn't very good at that point, so it was easy to choose to leave. But then I began having second thoughts. I thought maybe I could come back and convince her to run away with me. Then I saw her with Young. I watched them for a few days, and my anger grew with each day."

"Then tonight you couldn't handle it, I suppose. You

followed Theresa and Young back to the Empire, to her room," Mickey noted.

"That's right. I did follow them. I was angry and jealous. Young had no right to be with her, and I couldn't stand to see her with someone else."

"So, it looks like we both have secrets we don't want others to know about," said Mickey.

"I guess that's right. And if it gets out that I have been here, well, I won't go down alone. I won't hold back on revealing your secret if it comes down to it."

As they talked, Mickey had difficulty suppressing her attraction to him. It was a feeling she had previously; maybe it was part of the reason she was so willing to loan him the money. Well, that and the fact that Mickey wanted to protect her identity. But she knew it was more than the money. Mickey had often admired him at the Belmont. She watched him with customers. Her impression was that Nick was always kind and had a good sense of humor. Of course, he was pretty good looking too. But she couldn't let herself think like that then. She had to protect her identity, her job, her entire life in Butte. Now, things were different. Circumstances had changed. Besides, she had been growing increasingly tired of the stress of maintaining her secret. Maybe it was time to take a chance to get away from the lie of a life she had been living for the past few years.

"Well, maybe we can help each other out," she responded.

"What do you mean?"

"We both have secrets that we can't have exposed. As far as I know, we are the only ones that know each other's secrets. We both have a lot to lose if they come out."

"So, what do you propose?"

"What if we were to help each other? What if we both flee the area, far away, together?"

"Together?" Nick responded with great surprise.

"Yes, together. I am tired of living a lie. I am ready to restart my life again, to return to the real me – the woman I long to be, am meant to be. I have tried to live the life I felt forced to live, but I don't want that life anymore."

Stunned, Nick didn't respond for several minutes. What choices did he have? Nick needed to get out of Butte and quickly. And he needed to take his secrets with him. Leaving with Mickey might be his best option – possibly, his only option.

Chapter 41

On the Run

We have got to get out of here and fast, Nick thought to himself. He could not allow anyone to recognize him. Pulling his Fedora down a little lower and with his head down, he exited the M & M bar. The area was still busy with activity from people coming and going from the multiple bars and restaurants on Main Street. It would be easy to blend in. But he couldn't stay long. He must leave the area as quickly and quietly as possible. Returning to his hotel room, Nick gathered up his few belongings, checked out, and drove to Dublin Gulch to pick up Mickey before going down Main Street toward the highway leading out of Butte.

Mickey quickly left the M & M and went to her boarding room in Dublin Gulch. They had agreed that Nick would pick her up within the hour, so she had little time to gather her things. Mickey had accumulated a few things since coming to Butte, but very little was so valuable it couldn't be left behind. She retrieved the cash and jewelry she had hidden in her closet, put together a suitcase with clothes she felt she could quickly bring, and waited by the door for Nick to arrive in his car. Mickey felt guilty not saying goodbye to her friends in Dublin Gulch. But what could she say? It was best that she simply slipped away without anyone knowing. It would likely be several days before anyone would realize that she was gone – and by then, she and Nick Evans would be long gone. For several minutes she worried that Nick changed his mind and left without her. Suddenly she heard the sound of an approaching car and knew that it was Nick.

Driving west toward Anaconda, Nick wondered how Jeanne, Raymond and Mary were getting along. He had nothing against Mary or the children and was thankful for all that Mary had done in taking care of them. After all, by taking care of the children in Anaconda, she had made it possible for Theresa and Nick to manage the Belmont Bar in Butte. Of course, it didn't work out, but without Mary's willingness to take the children, they wouldn't have even had the opportunity to try. Jeanne wasn't his child, but he recognized that at age 13, life had been challenging for her. He had never really loved her but did feel a sense of concern and responsibility toward her. And Raymond had always been a challenge, full of mischief and frequently getting into trouble. He would not miss him. He briefly considered exiting into Anaconda to check on them but knew that doing so would be too risky. And of course, Mickey agreed. Nick decided they couldn't let anyone know where they were going or in which direction they fled Butte. Instead, they bypassed Anaconda, continued west until Garrison Junction, and then north toward McDonald Pass and Helena.

Just as they reached Helena, the morning news came over the car radio. The reporter said, "The Butte Police are investigating an incident that occurred late last night at the Empire Hotel. There is a report that a woman was beaten in her room and is in critical condition. Police indicate they are questioning a suspect but are not releasing any names at this time."

"I think it would be wise for us to hide out for a couple of days," Mickey said to Nick. "I doubt anyone is looking for us, but maybe hiding out for a few days will allow things to calm down a bit."

Nick thought to himself for a minute. Escaping to Canada was the overall plan, but as far as he knew, no one suspected him or knew he had even returned to Butte. A few days, hiding out wasn't such a bad idea. After all, no one had recognized him or knew that Mickey was gone. "Maybe you're right. No one has any reason to suspect us of anything, and the police have a suspect in custody for questioning. Neither Ivankovich nor Detective Duggan knows I have been in town. I think we are safe for a couple of days here, and then we can move on to Canada."

Two days later, they left their hiding spot in Helena and continued to Great Falls, planning to travel through Shelby on their way to the Canadian Border. If all went well, the day after tomorrow, they would be in Canada.

Chapter 42

Anaconda

The cold wind had whipped through Anaconda all day. It was Friday morning, and Jeanne and Raymond were expected home from school for lunch any minute. Mary had been busy preparing a hot lunch of soup and a sandwich for them when the doorbell rang.

"Mary Green?"

"Yes," she replied to the police officer standing at her door.

"I am Officer McGeever. I received a call from the Butte Police Department a short time ago. I am afraid I have some bad news."

Mary immediately knew it had to be about Theresa. She hadn't heard from her in a few weeks but was aware that she and Nick had lost the Belmont, that Nick had runoff, and that Theresa was living at the Empire Hotel. Mary had tried to get Theresa to come back to Anaconda, to get away from Butte and spend some time with her and the children. She hadn't told Jeanne and Raymond, not wanting to get their hopes up. And it was a good thing that Mary hadn't. Theresa had told Mary that she wasn't ready to give up. She was sure she could make it work in Butte. Theresa just needed some time. And of course, she was hoping, at least initially, that Nick would return. But she gave up on that hope a few months ago. Mary tried to convince her that Jeanne and

Raymond needed their mother, that going through adolescence was hard enough on its own, but without either parent, it was that much more difficult. Mary could only do so much to help them through it. She also could see that it was taking a toll on Jeanne. Jeanne had become more reclusive, more introverted. She didn't spend much time with friends now. Jeanne worked hard in school and with her after school job at the cafe inside the Montana Hotel. She was focused on working hard, a distraction from the emotional difficulties she was experiencing. It seemed it was the best way for her to cope with living apart from a mother or father.

Mary hesitantly responded, "Is this about my daughter? Is she all right?"

"I am afraid not, Mrs. Greene. She is in the county hospital in Butte, and it doesn't look good. I think you should go as soon as you can."

"What happened? Has she been in an accident?"

"I would rather not give any details, but I can tell you that she appears to be the victim of a violent attack. The Butte police will share more details when you arrive. But, please don't delay."

Mary was stunned. Who would do such a thing? She was not aware of any enemies that Theresa may have had. She had never mentioned anyone to her anyway. Was it just a random attack? Not likely. She surmised it must have had something to do with Nick. She decided it was best not to share anything with Jeanne until she knew more. After asking her sister Ursula to come over to finish preparing lunch for Jeanne and Raymond, she jumped in the car and took off for the 30-mile drive to Butte.

Mary barely recognized her daughter. Her face badly beaten to the point that she was nearly unrecognizable. Lying on the bed in intensive care with tubes attached and machines all around her, Mary wouldn't have known it was her had they not told her. Until she looked closely at her eyes. They were bruised and swollen, but a mother knows her children. The face disfigured, but those eyes were undoubtedly Theresa's.

Very quickly, her thoughts turned to Jeanne and Raymond. How was she going to tell them? What could she say? How do you tell a very vulnerable thirteen-year-old girl and her younger brother that their mother had been severely beaten and probably wasn't going to make it? There was no easy or right way. Torn between staying with her daughter and going to share the news with the children, Mary couldn't decide what to do. She reasoned that she was the one from whom Jeanne and Raymond needed to hear what happened to their mother. Besides, Theresa remained unconscious. The best thing to do was drive back to Anaconda, break the news to the children, arrange for someone in the family to stay with them and return to Butte in the morning. Hopefully, there would be enough time before...no, she wasn't willing to consider that yet.

As she pulled into the parking spot in front of the house, Mary saw Jeanne standing at the front door.

"Gramma, where have you been? Ursula said you had something suddenly come up and had to leave for a while. She wouldn't tell me what it was about but said you would explain it when you got home. Is everything okay?"

"Honey, get Raymond and sit down." They took their seats. "I have some bad news. Your mother is in the hospital in Butte."

"Is she going to be okay? What happened?" Jeanne asked cautiously.

Mary responded, "I am afraid she isn't doing very well. Someone attacked her and beat her severely. Your mother is in the hospital and has been unconscious since found in her room. At this point, they don't know for sure who did it, but they have a suspect in custody. Jeanne and Raymond, I hate to have to tell you, but the doctors don't think she is going to make it."

Stunned, Jeanne wasn't sure how to react. Tears filled her eyes, but no sound escaped her. It had been weeks since she had seen or heard from her mother, and she had developed a protective shell. She had been disappointed and abandoned so many times and left to feel unimportant. Yet, this was her mother. A mother she still loved despite all that she had gone through. She stood and quietly walked into her room and closed the door. Picking up the picture of her mother from the nightstand, she looked intently at it. And then the tears flowed. They flowed until she had no tears left. Finally, she prayed to God that her mother would make it, and then she drifted off to sleep.

Chapter 43

Butte

The morning edition of the Montana Standard on April 20, 1940, had a short article which read in part: "Mrs. Marie T. Evans, 37, former co-proprietor with her husband, Nick Evans, of the Belmont Bar, is near death as a result of an alleged beating Thursday night in her room at a local hotel. Police arrested D.C. Young, about 45, who has been employed here as a chef."

As Duggan read the article while sipping his morning coffee, he focused his attention on Theresa Evans and her assailant. There must be clues as to what happened based on the condition of her body. There were too many questions and not enough answers as to what happened at the Empire the previous evening.

Arriving at the office of Dr. Frank Williams, a receptionist greeted Detective Duggan. Showing her his badge, he said, "I need to talk with Dr. Williams, is he in?"

"Yes, he is, detective, he is just finishing up with his last patient for the morning. If you have a seat, I will let him know you are here."

About 10 minutes later, Duggan was brought back to the office of Dr. Williams.

"Thank you for seeing me, Dr. Williams. I understand you were called to the Empire Hotel to see Theresa Evans yesterday."

"That is correct. I was called and told someone was strangling at the Empire Hotel. I went immediately and found when I arrived that it was Theresa Evans."

"Can you tell me what you found when you arrived?"

"When I arrived, there were three ladies there; Mrs. Graham, a welfare worker whose name I don't recall, and another woman whose name I also don't remember. And of course, Mrs. Evans."

"What was her condition at that time?

"It was clear she had a brain disturbance, a hemorrhage."

"Any signs of physical violence?"

"Yes. She had blackened eyes, her face was badly swollen and bruised, and she was unconscious."

"What did you do then?" Duggan asked.

"There was nothing I could do for her there. I had the welfare worker call for an ambulance and had her transported to the county hospital."

"Dr. Williams, did you see anyone else there? Any males?"

"I didn't see any if they were there."

"Is there anything else you can add that might be helpful?"

"There is one more thing – she had been on the bed for some length of time because she had a voluntary passage of urine and bowel."

"And what time did you come to the Empire?"

"It was around 11:30."

"I have one more question, Dr. Williams. If her face was so swollen and bruised, how could you be sure that it was Theresa Evans?"

"I had been treating Mrs. Evans for an ulcer on her thigh earlier this year. I went on vacation to California for several weeks, and when I returned last week, she came to see me. I checked the ulcer, and it was nearly healed, just a scab. When I examined her yesterday, I checked, and the scab was there so I could confirm it was her."

Duggan then left Dr. Williams' office and went to the hospital to see Dr. J.L. Mundloch, the doctor who attended to Theresa Evans when she arrived at the hospital. He wanted to confirm that his description of the condition of her body was consistent with what Dr. Williams described.

"Thank you for seeing me, Dr. Mundloch. I know you are busy, so I won't take much of your time, but can you describe to me the condition of Theresa Evans when she arrived at the hospital yesterday?"

"Sure. Mrs. Evans was brought in by ambulance and was still on the stretcher when I saw her. She was unconscious, not breathing freely, and she apparently had been struck over the left eye. I then did a thorough examination and found she had multiple bruises on her body, including her breast, arms, and thorax. These were in addition to those on her face. Her pupils were irregular, the right eye dilated, pulse very rapid. She looked rather morbid, I must say."

"And what did you conclude based on the examination?"

"I concluded that she had a cerebral hemorrhage as a

result of the injuries sustained."

"All those bruises, how long do you think they were probably there?"

"Bruises generally take 12-24 hours to appear after an injury, but I can't be sure how long these were there."

"Is it possible that trauma the evening before you examined her, the afternoon of the next day, would result in those bruises?"

"Absolutely, it is possible," replied Dr. Mundloch.

Chapter 44

As Duggan considered all that the witnesses told him, clearly things weren't adding up. Young's recanting of the evening had too many holes. He had acted confused and was undoubtedly influenced by whatever he had been drinking last night and into the morning. And several hours were unaccounted for in his story. Where had he gone when he was supposed to be getting a doctor? He disappeared for at least two hours before returning. And what happened from the evening hours when witnesses said they saw them together, until seven in the morning when Marian Grant found her in her room groaning and foaming at the mouth? It was time to have another talk with Cabby Young.

"I understand that you and Theresa had drinks and did some dancing at the Belmont Bar last evening," Duggan said to Cabby.

"That is correct. She twisted her ankle during the evening, and so I helped her back to her room at the Empire."

"How long did you stay there?"

"Well, after we got to her room, I checked out her ankle. She said it was feeling much better, but she started complaining of heart trouble, at least that's what she said it was. But she didn't seem very sick to me, so I decided to go for a walk."

"You went for a walk? Where did you go?"

"I went over to the Belmont Bar, a couple of blocks

away. My friend is a bartender and was starting his shift at noon."

"And what is your friend's name?'

"Ed Deanne. I stayed there until about three or four o'clock. You can ask him, he knows."

"I will be talking with Mr. Deanne; you can be sure of that. What did you do after leaving the Belmont at around four o'clock?"

"I went back to see Theresa. When I got to her room, she was lying there, unconscious. At first, I thought she was just drunk, but she kept getting worse and worse. I got scared, so I tried to get a hold of a doctor. He just came in and said, "She'll be all right." So I got half-mad and called the policeman, I guess."

"So, you called the doctor?"

"Yes, well, I had the girl call."

"But then you left?"

"I went and called the police."

"You said you had been to the Belmont Bar. What time did you return to Theresa's room?

"Around 3:30 in the morning."

"What time did you go to the Belmont?"

"I don't remember exactly, but around midnight."

"And she didn't have any bruises when you left?"

"Oh yes, she had bruises on her body."

"But not on the face, her eyes?"

"No. Not until I came back around 3:30."

"So, you didn't call a doctor when you found her that way?"

"I tried, but I couldn't find one. His office said he

wouldn't be in until around eleven."

"What was her condition when you arrived around 3:30?"

"She was beaten up. She couldn't hear or talk. She couldn't tell me what happened."

"Let's get back to when you left around midnight. You went to the Belmont, is that correct?"

"Yes. I visited my friend Ed Deanne who started his shift then."

"What about this bottle of Muscatel in her room? Did you drink it together?

"Yes. Earlier, in the afternoon."

"Did you both drink it?"

"Yes."

"Did you two argue, a fight? Did you then beat her up?"

"No, sir. I would never beat her."

"Have you ever been in trouble before Mr. Young? Spend time in prison?"

"Yeah, in Boise. Lived in Idaho Falls at the time."

"No other trouble?"

"Just some minor things. Drinking, fighting, that kind of thing."

"Can you imagine who might have done this to her if you didn't?"

"The only thing I can imagine is when I asked her a week or so ago what had happened, she said she fought with a lady friend."

"Did she have any bruises on her face when you saw her then?"

"No, sir."

"And how about when you saw her around midnight. Did she have any facial bruises then?"

"No, sir. And I didn't ask her who her friend was that she fought with previously."

"Ok. Now back to when you first found that Theresa had been beaten. Was there anyone else there?"

"Yes. Billie Grant. At least that is how she was introduced to me, but I guess her real name is Marion."

"Is that the first time you met Miss Grant?"

"No, I met her last night. We all had a few drinks in Theresa's room together. Me, Theresa, and Billie. It was around nine. Then I left for a while."

"I thought you said you left around midnight, went to the Belmont?"

"I guess it was around midnight because that is when my friend Ed started his shift at the bar."

Things were still not adding up, thought Duggan. He said to Young, "Of course we are going to have to hold you until we know whether she is going to live or die. There is nothing we can do until her condition determines what our course will be."

Chapter 45

Duggan contacted the county hospital for an update on Theresa Evans' condition. A message had been left for him from the hospital to call as soon as he arrived at his office. More than 48 hours since the apparent attack on her, he was told that she never regained consciousness and expired at 2:05 that morning, April 21. They now had a probable murder and a prime suspect in custody. Cabby Young would not be released today and maybe never. Duggan knew convicting the killer would be much more difficult now that the prime witness had died without being able to identify the assailant.

The Montana Standard morning edition read: "Marie T. Evans died in the county hospital early today without regaining consciousness from injuries suffered at the hands of an unknown assailant after being brutally beaten. D.C. Young is being held in the county jail for investigation in connection with the case."

An autopsy was performed on Mrs. Marie Theresa Green Evans at 2 p.m. on April 22, 1940, at the Lavis Merrill Mortuary in Anaconda. Drs. Donich and McMahon were present in addition to A.C. Longfellow, mortician. The stated cause of death was a subdural hemorrhage over the right cerebral hemisphere, causing pressure on the brain and eventual death.

Due to the suspicious nature of Theresa Evans' death and the potential for murder, Coroner Con Sheehy called for an Inquest. Held on the 25th and 26th of April

1940, six men served on the jury, and D.C. Young was the focus of the Inquiry.

Among those called to testify was the lead person conducting the autopsy, Dr. E.S. McMahon. The autopsy report, read by Dr. McMahon, said in part, "There were multiple bruises scattered over the body, especially prominent on the arms, head, face, and legs. The left eye area was much discolored and, in ordinary English, referred to as a marked black eye. There was an old draining wound, the site of an old infection four inches above the right knee on the anterior aspect of the thigh. There was a possible fracture of the right ankle."

During testimony, Dr. McMahon was asked his conclusion as to the cause of the hemorrhage.

"I would say due to violence," he responded.

Asked to explain the nature of a contrecoup concussion, he responded that if a person sustained a blow to one side of the head, it is possible to experience damage on the opposite side, including a hemorrhage.

"Is it your opinion that it was the situation in this case?" asked the prosecuting attorney.

"Yes, sir."

"The fact that there was no hemorrhage in the brain itself eliminates disease of hardening of the arteries?"

"Yes, it should," Dr. McMahon responded.

In cross-examination, when asked if the bruises on the body were old bruises, he testified that, in his opinion, they were not. They were likely a couple of days but no more than a week old.

"Could the hemorrhage have been caused by a fall?"

"It could," he replied.

"Or by striking?"

"Yes, sir."

"But is it your opinion that a person could not receive the multiple bruises which you found on Theresa Evans by an ordinary fall?"

"I don't think so," concluded Dr. McMahon.

Testimony then turned to A.E. Longfellow, mortician. Asked to describe the body of Mrs. Evans at the autopsy, he indicated it to be much the same as Dr. McMahon's description.

"Mr. Longfellow. Were the bruises you found old bruises?"

"I would judge probably two or three days."

"They couldn't be longer than that, could they?"

"I hardly think so because, in the injection of the embalming fluid, most of the discoloration cleared considerably, showing that the blood was not so severely coagulated and dried."

"So, the bruises were two or three days old? All the bruises on her body?"

"Yes, sir."

They then called Mrs. Margaret Bowers to testify.

"Were you at the Empire Hotel on April 19, 1940?"

"I was coming there about 7:10 in the morning and got to the first floor when someone said there was a commotion, so don't go up there. I was going back out and met Mr. Young running out. He said to get a doctor. He had a ruffled collar, and his tie was not on straight."

"Do you know whether or not Mr. Young had been

drinking?"

"I couldn't say."

"Did you know what the commotion was about or where Mr. Young went to?"

"No, sir."

"Did you see him coming down the street?"

'Yes, sir," stated Mrs. Bowers.

The State of Montana then called Miss Lily Hoar as a witness. Miss Hoar was a stenographer for the County's Attorney's Office. She confirmed that she recorded the statements of D. C. Young, in response to questioning by County Attorney J.F. Emigh, concerning the evidence surrounding the death of Theresa Evans.

The attorney asked her to read the statements Young made to the questions asked.

"Mr. Young, will you tell us just what happened the night before last? Tell us everything you know," asked the lead attorney for the State of Montana.

"Well, during the evening, she complained about heart trouble, but she didn't seem so very sick, so I said that I thought I'd go for a walk. She didn't feel so good, but I didn't think it was too bad."

"So, you went for a walk?"

"Yes, I went over to the Belmont Bar."

"How long did you stay?"

"Oh, I stayed until about three or four o'clock, I guess, and when I came back here, she was lying unconscious. I thought at first that she was just drunk, but she kept getting worse and worse. I got scared, so I tried to get hold of a doctor, and he just came in and looked around, and I said, "Why don't you do something?" And he said, "She'll be all right." So I got half-mad and called the policeman, I guess."

"Did you call the doctor?"

"Yes, well, I had the girl call."

"But then you left?"

"Well, I went down and called the policeman."

"What time did you get back to the room from the Belmont Bar?"

"Oh, I would say about 3:30."

"In the morning?"

"Yes, in the morning."

"When did you go there (Belmont)?"

"I don't know exactly. Around midnight, I think."

"And she didn't have any bruises when you left?"

"Oh, yes, she had bruises on the body when I left."

"On the body, but not on the throat and eye?"

"No."

"Did she have bruises on her throat and eye when you came back at 3:30?"

"Yes."

"But you didn't get a doctor then?" questioned the attorney.

"I couldn't find any. I went all over town, and the only thing I could find out was that they (the doctor) wouldn't be there till about eleven."

"Who did you get?"

"The city doctor, Dr. Williams."

"When you left at midnight, she was asleep in the room?"

"Trying to sleep."

"She was in bed and sick, correct?"

"Yes."

"And when you came back about 3:30, you found her beaten up?"

"Yes. She couldn't hear, she couldn't speak, she couldn't tell me what happened."

"Who did you talk to between midnight and 3:30?"

"Eddie Deane. He goes on shift at midnight."

"Then, he should know you were in there until about 3:30?"

"Yes."

"You are sure you did not fight with her? Beat up on her?

"No, sir. I never beat her."

"Her face was alright – no bruises – when you first met her yesterday?"

"Yes."

"And her face was all right at midnight when you left her?"

"Yes, sir."

"Now, you stated yesterday that you went out about eight and stayed till midnight?"

"Did I? Well, it must have been midnight because the night shift bartender was on shift, and he comes on at midnight."

"Were you at the ABC Bar after midnight?"

"Yes. Just long enough to get a drink. Then I went back to the Belmont Bar."

The testimony of C.A. Young then concluded. There

were many inconsistencies and conflicts in his statements, both in his testimony and compared to others' testimony. It would now be left to the inquest jury to decide the role of Cabby Young in the death of Theresa Evans. The county prosecutor awaited their decision.

Chapter 46

Mary Green had arrived at the county hospital in Butte just after 7 a.m. She had received a call from the hospital around 3 a.m. The news was not good but anticipated. She hadn't expected her daughter to make it based on all that the medical personnel had told her. She was hoping that Theresa would regain consciousness long enough to recognize her and to say goodbye, but after spending many hours at her bedside the past day and a half, it became clear that she was unlikely to do so. She was also hoping that she would be able to identify the perpetrator and bring some semblance of justice to this ordeal. But it was not to be. Marie Theresa Evans died without regaining sufficient consciousness to speak coherently. Mary heard her mumble on several occasions, but it wasn't clear or even recognizable. She wanted to believe she was calling out to her and her children, but it was probably just wishful thinking. No, sadly, the last days of Marie Theresa Evans were without coherence or ability to communicate. But it was over. She was no longer suffering. Now there was no pain, or fear, or anxiety about her future. Nor was there the opportunity to say a final farewell to her family. The end had come to a life full of inconsistency, doubt, uncertainty, unfulfilled potential, and failed relationships. At the young age of thirty-seven years, Theresa Evans passed, leaving behind a thirteen-year-old daughter and ten-year-old son to manage through life without parents. But thank God for the love and dedication of a grandmother.

Chapter 47

The Coroner's Inquest of Marie Theresa Evans completed on April 26, 1940. Coroner Con Sheahy presented his case regarding D. C. Young and concluded with these instructions to the six-member all-male jury: "Gentleman of the Jury, being now there is no further evidence to submit to you, I will now present the case to you for your consideration, and when you have arrived at the same you will report to me at once."

The following day, Coroner Sheahy received the decision of the jury. The written report read as follows:

Verdict

That the said, Mrs. Marie Theresa Evans was injured on or about April 19th, 1940, and the date of her death was April 21st, 1940, at County Hospital, Silver Bow County, Montana.

Cause of death: subdural hemorrhage over the right cerebral hemisphere causing pressure on the brain and eventually death.

That the said, Mrs. Marie Theresa Evans came to her death by a person or persons unknown to the jury.

This all happened in Silver Bow County, State of Montana.

Jack Duggan was shocked. He was sure that the jury would come back with a verdict that would at least lead the county prosecutor to try C.A. Young in the death of Theresa Evans before a formal jury. Sure, there was conflicting and contradictory evidence, but it seemed to Duggan that the preponderance of evidence pointed to Young as the killer. Maybe Duggan was missing something. Maybe there was more information that had not come out yet. Perhaps somebody else knew something that would lead to another suspect. But he had an idea who.

Duggan caught Ed Deanne just as he was getting off shift at the Belmont.

"You got a few minutes Deanne?" Duggan said.

"I can spare a few before I go home. What about?"

"The Theresa Evans case," replied Duggan.

"Yeah, I heard the jury from the inquest didn't find Cabby Young guilty."

"Well, that is why I want to talk to you. You were working that night at the Belmont. Did you notice anything suspicious or see anything out of the ordinary that night?"

"Now that you mention it, I noticed a couple of odd things around the time Theresa and Cabby left the bar."

"Like what?" asked Duggan.

"Just a minute or so after they left the bar, a gentleman followed behind them. I didn't recognize him, don't recall seeing him around here before."

"Can you describe him?"

"I didn't get a good look at his face. He had a fedora pulled down low on his head, and he was wearing dark glasses. I guess that is why I took notice. It was a little strange seeing somebody wearing dark glasses in the evening."

"That is odd. And you didn't think to mention it before?"

"I guess I didn't think it was important then. But there is something else. Right after the guy walked out, a regular patron followed out quickly after him."

"And who was that? Asked Duggan.

"Mickey McCarthy," came Deanne's reply.

Duggan was perplexed. Who was the mystery man? He figured the best way to find out was to pay a visit to Mickey McCarthy. He knew that Mickey was living in Dublin Gulch, which was about a half-mile from the Belmont Bar. Before arriving in Dublin Gulch, he stopped at Maloney's Bar to find out in which boarding room she lived.

"Maloney, I am looking for Mickey McCarthy. Any idea where I can find him?"

"I can tell you where he was living, but nobody has seen him for over a week now. His place is empty, and no one seems to know where he has gone. He hasn't shown up for work all week, either. Mike McGee says he saw him at the M & M the night of the Theresa Evans beating with some guy, but nobody has seen him since," replied Maloney.

"Where can I find McGee?" Duggan asked.

"That's him at the end of the bar."

"Mike McGee? I am Detective Duggan. I understand you saw Mickey McCarthy with a guy the night of Theresa Evans beating."

"That's right. Must have been after midnight. I noticed this guy come in and sit down at the bar. He looked a little frazzled. Then McCarthy came in shortly afterward and struck up a conversation with him. Can't tell you what they said since they went over to a back table," reported McGee.

"How long were they there?" Duggan asked.

"Must have been a half-hour, forty-five minutes at the most."

"Did they leave together?"

"Yeah. It sounded like some kind of plan was made. I heard the other guy tell McCarthy that he would pick him up within the hour. It was about the only thing I heard them say as they walked passed me towards the door."

"Can you describe the other guy?"

"Dark glasses. Fedora. Thin mustache. That's about all I remember," replied McGee.

That is the same description Deanne gave of the man he saw leave the Belmont after Theresa Evans and Young, thought Duggan. Who was this man? Who would have a reason to follow them, and why?

"Wait a minute McGee. You said you heard them both speak, is that right?" Duggan asked.

"That's right."

"Tell me something, did the man have an accent?

"Many people around here have an accent. But it wasn't a typical accent I hear. It certainly wasn't Irish or Italian. Sounded a bit different, eastern European if I had to make a guess," McGee responded.

Could it be, Duggan thought to himself. "Have you ever met that fellow that used to run the Belmont Bar a while back?"

"Been in the Belmont a few times but never met the managers. But I do recall hearing them talk. She had a normal English accent, but he had an unusual accent..." he trailed off as if trying to place it.

"Maybe eastern European?" Duggan asked.

McGee nodded. "The same as the man talking with McCarthy."

Chapter 48

Duggan had to find McCarthy. He was sure he could lead him to the mystery man and potentially the murderer of Theresa Evans. He still wasn't convinced Young hadn't done it, but now there was another suspect...or maybe two.

He went to Dublin Gulch and found the boarding room where McCarthy was living. There was no sign of him, and several neighbors said they had not seen any sign of him in over a week. After getting a search warrant, Duggan returned. When he entered the apartment, the condition suggested McCarthy had left in a hurry. The kitchen table still held utensils, and salt, pepper and sugar containers. The kitchen sink had dirty dishes. His bed was left messy, the closet door and the dresser drawers were left open. Some clothing remained, and it appeared as though he grabbed whatever he could take in a hurry. There was no indication of foul play or forced entry. It was apparent that Mickey McCarthy left of his own volition and in a hurry.

Where had McCarthy gone, and who was the mystery man with whom she likely left? The more Duggan thought about it, the more he felt the man was probably Nick Evans. Both Ed Deanne, the bartender at the Belmont Bar, and Mike McGee described an eastern European accent. That certainly sounded like Nick Evans. Sure, there were a few others in Butte with a similar accent. Still, when he put it together with the other evidence, it pointed to Evans – he is familiar with the Belmont Bar, probably chasing after his wife and Young, and has a known association with McCarthy. Granted, he hadn't been seen since his disappearance several months ago, and no one knew where he had gone. Obviously, this man had been disguising himself with the fedora and dark glasses, A few other changes with hairstyle and facial hair, and he could undoubtedly pass himself off as someone else for a while. It had to be Nick Evans.

After a thorough search of Butte, Duggan was confident that Nick Evans and Mickey McCarthy left town together. But where had they gone, and in which direction? They could have gone south toward Idaho Falls, east toward Bozeman, west toward Missoula, or north toward Helena. Duggan reasoned that if they were on the run, especially if they had committed a serious crime such as murder, they would have headed north toward the Canadian border. The last time anyone saw them was six days ago at Maloney's bar. Duggan contacted police departments throughout the area with descriptions of the two. He had no idea what type of vehicle they were driving as it was likely Evans purchased a car when he was on the run the first time. Finding them was going to be difficult, he realized.

Late that afternoon, Duggan received a call from a Powell County deputy.

"Detective Duggan, this is Deputy Meyer from Powell County. I may have a lead on that case of the two missing people from Butte you are on the hunt for."

"What have you got, Meyer?" Duggan asked excitedly.

"I got a call a few minutes ago from a clerk at a gas station at Garrison Junction. He said he saw two people getting gas a few days ago, one of which fit the description you sent."

"What did he say about them?"

"Well, he said one of them spoke with an unusual accent, wore dark glasses, and a fedora."

"What about the other one?"

"He said the other one was a woman. But she had unusually short hair. He didn't think anything of it until he heard that there was a hunt on for two people. The clerk said he understood it was two men, but after thinking about the woman's unusually short hair, he thought he better at least contact me."

Nick Evans pulled into a gas station in Vaughn, Montana, in the early evening. Vaughn was a small town north of Great Falls, where he felt safe stopping. There were a couple of small motels, and they were both exhausted. He decided they should get some rest for a few hours and then continue north toward Canada. They slept until 6 a.m., showered, and went to a cafe for coffee and a bite to eat. As Nick was paying for the coffee and food, Mickey tapped him on the shoulder and said, "We better get out of here."

She was holding a copy of the Great Falls Tribune. The back page headline read: Butte Police looking for two murder suspects on the run.

The accompanying article went on to describe the

two suspects. One is a man believed to have been in disguise but has an eastern European accent and last seen wearing a fedora and dark glasses. The other is a woman with a short, man's haircut, believed to have been posing as a man previously. Thankfully there were no pictures. Nick had discarded the Fedora and glasses yesterday, replacing them with a pork pie hat. Mickey looked much different than when they left Butte, but now with the description in the paper, she put on a felt turban-style hat to cover her short hair.

They calmly left the store and then quickly gathered their things. "We need to get a different vehicle and soon," said Nick. "Somebody must have seen us and gave a description. They may have seen the car too. I hope we didn't make a big mistake by staying in Helena."

They decided to trade the 1932 Ford Coupe for a 1935 Studebaker Champion. They were able to make a quick sale at a used car lot in Cascade, and soon they were on the road north again. With any luck, they would be safe in Canada by nightfall.

Duggan knew he didn't have a lot of time. The more hours that passed, the less likely he was to find Evans and McCarthy. The gas station attendant had thought they went east from Garrison Junction but couldn't be sure. It made sense to Duggan that they would go north if they were planning to escape to Canada. He made calls to police departments in Helena and Great Falls, but there were no reports of seeing the fugitives. Perhaps he was wrong. Maybe they went west toward

Missoula first and then headed north. Calls to Missoula and Kalispell also came up empty.

He was about to give up hope when he got a call the next afternoon from an officer in Shelby, Montana.

"Good afternoon Detective Duggan. I am Officer Bloomquist calling from Shelby about the fugitives you guys are looking for."

"What do you have?" asked Duggan.

"It might not be much, but a farmer near here called and said he was nearly run off the road by a car heading north from Shelby this morning. He was driving his tractor up the highway to get to his field, and this car came up behind him and nearly clipped him as they sped around. He barely kept the tractor out of the ditch."

"Did he get a description of the vehicle?'

"Said it was a Studebaker, probably 3 or 4 years old. Looked like two people inside."

"Any chance you can put an officer in pursuit?" Duggan asked.

"Sorry, detective, we are low on staff up here and can't keep up now. I would suggest you contact border control at Sweet Grass to see if they can help."

Sweet Grass was the last spot in Montana north of Shelby before crossing into Canada and was less than 50 miles away. Duggan made a call to border control right away.

"This is Detective Duggan from the Butte Police Department. I am looking for two suspects in a murder case traveling in a 1934 or 35 Studebaker. I have reason to believe they are heading north in your area."

"We had a couple come through about an hour or so ago in a Studebaker. Nice couple. Said they were traveling to Canada on their honeymoon and would be back in a few days."

For a minute or two, Duggan considered all that happened over the past several days and his options. He had been working feverishly to track Evans and McCarthy down. Realizing he likely lost his suspects, he simply said, "thank you" and hung up the receiver.

Epilogue

Mary Green, my great grandmother, continued to live in Anaconda after Theresa Evans died. She passed away on March 5, 1963. Jeanne continued to live with her grandmother in Anaconda until graduating from St. Peter's Catholic High School in 1944. Soon after, she married William C. Klein, and together they had a child, my oldest sister Marie. Their marriage was short-lived. Then mom, at age 20, married my dad, John W. Ohman, on March 15, 1947. My dad adopted Marie in 1956. John and Jeanne Ohman went on to have ten children together, of which I am number seven of the eleven. Mom and dad raised us in Anaconda, except for a couple of years with their youngest two daughters in Coeur D'Alene, Idaho, and their final few years in Butte.

Mom continued to be a very hard worker throughout her life. Early in her marriage, she worked as a waitress. She continued to do so on and off for many years. In 1957 mom and dad opened an A&W franchise in Deer Lodge, Montana, followed by purchasing an existing one in Anaconda in 1963. They also operated one for a short time in Virginia City, Montana, beginning in 1959. In those years, the A&Ws were open in just the summer months. In 1966, they started Granny's Pizza in Anaconda adjacent to the A&W and owned both until they retired in 1975. Dad also owned and operated the Anaconda Disposal Service for several years in the late 1950s and early 1960s, as well as periodically working at the smelter over many years. Both worked very hard, making the businesses and family successful. Most of us children worked at the A&W and Granny's while growing up. We all developed a strong work ethic from our parents.

My dad passed away on December 22, 2001. Mom passed away four years later, on November 9, 2005. It is somewhat ironic that after living nearly her entire life in Anaconda, she died in Butte, the city in which her mother, Theresa Evans, was murdered some 65 years earlier.

Throughout her life, mom remained reluctant to share about her childhood and the events surrounding her mother's murder. She never offered information and was reticent to answer questions posed by her children. When she did respond, it was usually concise and without detail. We asked more questions many times, but mom typically ended the questioning pretty abruptly. Even up to the time of her death, she offered very little regarding the death of her mother or her childhood experiences. I am not sure how much detail she truly knew about the murder and the surrounding event. I suspect that her grandmother and other family members kept details from her to protect her since she was so young at the time.

I can't help but believe that the difficulties and challenges she faced as a child impacted her profoundly, shaping her entire outlook on life. I suspect having 11 children was at least partially the result of the inconsistent, unstable, and often lonely life she experienced as a child. Maybe, in her way, raising 11 children softened the experience she had as a child. She often said, "I wanted six kids, but I was doubly blessed."

Although mom rarely showed outward affection toward us, we knew she loved us without question. She and dad always worked hard and sacrificed for us so that we never lacked for anything we needed growing up. Raising eleven children was a challenge which they accepted and managed very well. Neither of my parents attended college or university, but they always encouraged us to continue our education. Nearly all of us attended or completed advanced education. I would argue that we are all very successful, each in his or her way. Our parents demonstrated a strong work ethic, and we all followed their example.

Characters for this book came from research, the limited answers mom provided to questions, and some creativity on my part. Most were actual people derived from the Coroner's Inquest testimony and other research I conducted. I developed a few characters from comments mom and others made about what they knew or heard. For example, Mickey McCarthy is a fictional character based on the rumor/suspicion that a woman working in the mines at the time was posing to be a man. This person may have had something to do with the murder, but to my knowledge and research, there is nothing to confirm this suspicion.

C.A. Young was the primary suspect, and based on the coroner's inquiry, the events unfolded as described in the book. The reason or reasons the jury did not find

Young guilty of the beating and subsequent death of Theresa Evans is unclear. I can only assume the jury determined the evidence insufficient to convict. I found no indication of any other suspects considered by the police department or that the county prosecutor considered the case any further. Apparently, after the inquest and the jury's verdict, the case was closed, and the killer of Theresa Evans remains unknown.

Not having many of the details, I used some creativity to develop Young's character more fully. But for the most part, the testimony recorded is accurate and taken directly from the Coroner's Inquest. The other witnesses included in this book are actual people, and their statements were recorded directly from the inquest. Some of the questioning done by Detective Duggan was created by me to fill in gaps or complete the story. I do not know what became of C.A. Young after the inquest concluded or the other people who testified.

Nickolas Evans was born in 1895 in Plevan, Bulgaria. I found no trace of him after Theresa Evans' death other than a death notice from Bulgaria. Although records have been hard to find, it is certainly possible, maybe even probable, that he returned to Bulgaria shortly after Theresa's death.

We will likely never know who killed Theresa Evans. You, the reader, have several suspects to consider. Was the killer C.A. Young, Nick Evans, Mickey McCarthy, or someone unknown?

Photos

Anaconda smelter

Anaconda cityscape

Anaconda miners

Anaconda Christmas tree on City Commons, 1937

Anaconda downtown

Montana Hotel and cafe

Anselmo mine

Duggan for sheriff

Butte Hill

Dublin Gulch

Dumas brothel

Empire Hotel/Copper Block

Finn Town

Venus Alley

CPSIA information can be obtained
at www.ICGtesting.com
Printed in the USA
BVHW091426031220
594765BV00010B/1339